the
MAGIC
MALA

A STORY THAT CHANGES LIVES

BOB OLSON

BBP

PUBLISHED BY BUILDING BRIDGES PRESS

Library of Congress Cataloging-in-Publication Data
    Olson, Bob
    The Magic Mala: A Story That Changes Lives / Bob Olson
    p. cm.
    1. Self-Help. 2. Literature & Fiction—Metaphysical & Visionary Fiction. 3. Self-Help—Personal Transformation. 4. New Age & Spirituality.

First Printing: May 2017
Printed in the USA

Cover design by Melissa Olson (concept) and BeSpoke Book Covers (design)
Interior Design & Typesetting by Colleen Sheehan of WDR Book Design

Library of Congress Control Number: 2017902485
ISBN: 978-0-9656019-1-7

BUILDING BRIDGES PRESS

Dedicated to my one and only love, Melissa.

Had she not rebelled against her curfew at age twelve, I might not have met her. Had she not been so smart and pretty, I might not have fallen in love so hard and so young. Had she not been so strong and supportive, I might not have survived my chronic depression in my twenties. Had she not encouraged me to believe in myself, I might not have persisted through the financial struggles of my thirties. Had she not believed in me, I might not have had the courage to pursue my dreams in my forties. Had she not worked with me side by side, I might not have been able to create such fulfilling work in my life. Had she not served as an example of what it means to be loving, compassionate, and kind, I might not be the man I have become today. And finally, if Melissa had not taught me to love myself, I might not have the love inside of me that I have for others. For this and so much more, I am the luckiest human being alive because of you, my sweet Melissa. You are undeniably and so reliably the love of my life.

CHAPTER ONE:

THE SEARCH

ROBBY ROBINSON waited until his wife, Mary, left for the store. He watched his high school sweetheart get into her twelve-year-old station wagon. The contrast between her natural beauty and the wagon's rusty exterior was painful to him. "She deserves so much more," he murmured to himself.

Fifteen years earlier, Mary had shown up in his neighborhood visiting a friend who lived there. The barefoot blonde caught Robby's eye and he was smitten. She liked him, too, but never expected that the popular junior class president would be interested in her. After all, he was two years older than she and had plenty of girls his own age who liked him. After that night, he only wanted one girl. He asked her on a date before the evening was over, and they dated for ten years before getting married.

As Mary drove down the street, Robby wondered where he'd gone wrong. He had planned on being a millionaire by thirty, but here it was two years later and his homecoming queen was driving a jalopy to the grocery store with the last of their money.

When her car turned the corner and was out of sight, he ran up the stairs to the second floor where the attic stairs were hidden in the hallway ceiling. He pulled the string above him and the stairs unfolded like an accordion toward the floor, dropping dust and frayed bits of insulation on his head. Robby climbed toward the attic to have a look around. He knew his 180-pound frame would easily make it through the ceiling hole, but he felt the steep climb in his legs from spending too much time sitting behind his computer.

There's got to be something up here of value I can pawn or sell, Robby thought as he hoisted himself through the hole into the sweltering early summer heat. After standing up and shaking the insulation out of his thick black hair, he was overwhelmed by all the boxes—lots and lots of boxes—and not one with a label of the contents inside. *This is going to take a while*, he decided, and then looking at his watch concluded, *I've got forty-five minutes to see what I can find.*

Wanting to avoid two hornets flying up by the skylight, Robby started with a small box at the opposite end of the attic. He chose it because it wasn't sealed shut. He spread open the cardboard flaps and peered inside. His face brightened.

Inside was the scrimshaw pocketknife he'd gotten as a grooms-man gift at the wedding of his buddy Kris. Next to the knife was an old watch with a cracked crystal that he had found at the beach. He liked it, and it kept accurate time, but he could never afford to get the crystal fixed. Beside that was a Montblanc pen that might have some value except he remembered it didn't work. He held it in his hand but couldn't recall how he had acquired it. Nonetheless, it was the same problem: he couldn't afford to get it working.

You have to have money to make money, he thought. *If I could get these two items repaired, I'd probably double my money by selling them.*

Robby threw the Montblanc pen back into the box. "What good are ya?" Pushing aside a Red Sox baseball cap that would be too small for him now, he saw an old hockey puck signed by Wayne Gretzky. "Ah, yes! Now we're talking."

Robby was a Bruins fan, but he idolized Wayne Gretzky of the Los Angeles Kings. He pulled the puck out and held it, recalling the memory of the night he'd gotten it nearly seventeen years prior.

His father had taken him to see the Great One in Los Angeles when he was fifteen years old on their trip to California. They were sitting behind the goal when Gretzky's shot hit the post, deflected over the safety glass, and Robby caught it. He recalled how it hurt his hand in the catch, but he didn't let on because his father was so proud of him.

Later, as they were leaving the arena, they spotted Gretzky peeking out of a doorway between the pizza and pretzel stands, apparently waiting for someone. Robby's dad nudged him to go ask for an autograph, which Gretzky might have ignored except that he saw Robby was wearing a Los Angeles Kings shirt with his number on it: 99.

Gretzky waved Robby and his father over behind the door and signed the puck. Robby's dad took a picture of them together with Gretzky holding it. It was one of the few times Robby and his father attended an event like this, and consequently, it was one of his favorite childhood memories.

I guess I'll see what I can get for it, Robby thought as he wiped the sweat off his forehead with his sleeve. *It's crazy hot up here. Is this what my life has come to, sweating my butt off in an attic for a few extra bucks?*

Robby scanned the attic and saw another box that wasn't sealed shut, a bigger one. It was located just under the hornets. He slowly moved toward the box realizing the hornets weren't paying attention; they just wanted to get outside.

"I don't blame you guys. How'd you get in here in the first place?" he said.

He cautiously grabbed the skylight handle and cranked it counterclockwise. The skylight window opened, and the hornets quickly escaped. Robby hastily closed the skylight tight again.

"You're welcome!" he yelled to the hornets that were now out of sight. "Thanks for not stinging me," he muttered.

Robby grabbed the big box that was on top of a file cabinet and placed it on the floor. He immediately spotted a cigar box of his father's inside. He pulled the cigar box out of the larger box and opened its lid to be greeted by the sweet aroma of cigars. Memories of his father smoking cigars while cooking steaks on the grill suddenly consumed him. He closed his eyes and held the memory there for a few seconds. Then he returned from the past and continued his search.

There was one cigar still in the box that crumbled in his fingers like dry wheat when he picked it up. The tobacco leaves stuck to his sweaty fingers. Suddenly his attention was drawn to what looked like blue rosary beads.

"Cool!" Robby slowly picked up the beads. "What happened to your cross?" He looked around the cigar box but saw no crucifix that might have fallen off the rosary.

This has some weight to it, he thought. *These stones must be real . . . and may be valuable. I wonder if these have sentimental value to Dad.*

As he held the beads, a chill ran down Robby's spine. He placed the beads next to the hockey puck and then examined the other contents of the cigar box. His eye was drawn to a little four-inch-by-three-inch booklet with the title *Your New Mala Manual*. He opened the booklet out of curiosity and began reading.

This mala (pronounced mah-lah) *is the key to unlocking your every desire. It has 108 beads and was hand strung in India. If this mala found its way to you, you have been blessed by great fortune. One does not choose a mala. The*

*mala chooses you. If you purchased this in a store, the mala
drew your attention to it. Congratulations. This magic mala
can and will change your life if used properly. This manual
will teach you how.*

Robby picked up the beads and stared at them in wonder.

"So you're not rosary beads," he said aloud. "You're mala beads,
whatever that means. A magic mala, apparently. You must have been
my dad's. Maybe that's why he has always been so successful." Robby
chuckled to himself.

Robby wasn't sure what to think about the mala, but he knew he
didn't believe in magic. He was a true skeptic, and everyone who knew
him was aware of it. It was kind of his image ever since taking a journalism class in college. "Believe in nothing that doesn't have evidence
to support it," his professor had taught. Robby respected that philosophy, so he'd adopted it as his own.

He glanced at his watch and saw that he'd already spent a half
hour looking around. He grabbed the hockey puck, mala beads, and
booklet and climbed down from the attic. He needed to cool down
and change his sweat-soaked shirt before Mary got home. He didn't
want her to know what he was up to. Even though she knew they
were three months late on the rent, he had assured her everything
was going to be all right. When they got married he had promised
her that she'd never have to worry about money. Yet now she was in
between jobs, his business was struggling, and Robby loathed the idea
of not keeping his promise.

CHAPTER TWO:

THE SACRIFICE

MARY LEFT THE grocery store and drove down the street to Jankowitz Jewelers. She had never been inside because she could never afford to shop there, but she had always wondered what it must be like to be around all that gorgeous jewelry. Even though she was a simple girl with simple tastes and didn't yearn for many luxuries in life, she loved nice jewelry. She just didn't own much of it.

Mary parked her car and turned off the engine, causing it to backfire so loudly that it sounded like a shotgun blast. Mary crouched down when passers-by looked in her direction. She then waited a few minutes out of embarrassment before she got out of her ailing station wagon.

Entering the jewelry store, Mary felt out of place. *They'll take one look at me and know I can't afford anything in here*, she assumed. An older woman behind the counter sat up from her desk and walked toward Mary with a friendly smile. "How are you today, dear?" asked the woman, whose name tag read *Eva*.

"I'm well, thank you. This is a beautiful store." Mary looked around at the glass counters filled with rings, bracelets, earrings, and watches placed on gray velvet. She saw diamonds, emeralds, rubies, sapphires, and other bright-colored gemstones she couldn't identify. The stones were placed in white and yellow gold settings that were perfectly displayed under lighting that made the whole store sparkle.

"Thank you," said Eva. "This is one of the oldest jewelry stores in Worcester. In fact, in the whole state of Massachusetts. Mr. Jankowitz is a third-generation goldsmith and gemologist." She leaned on the counter with a smile. "So, how might we help you today?"

Mary pulled a small, worn, white cardboard box out of her purse and placed it on the counter. She opened it to reveal an antique gold ring with rubies on either side of a great big diamond. "It was my mother's," she said. "She's now passed."

"I'm sorry for your loss, dear."

Mary shook her head. "No, not necessary. I was ten years old when she died. That was twenty years ago."

"The ring is extraordinary. Did you want to get it appraised?" asked Eva.

"Well, I was actually wondering if you might be interested in buying it."

"Let me get the owner, Mr. Jankowitz. He can help you with this. He's in his workshop, so I'll just be a moment."

The woman walked through a door that led to an area behind the retail space of the jewelry store, and Mary fidgeted nervously with the box. She picked up the ring and kissed it. "Sorry, Mom," she said quietly as she brushed a tear from her cheek. She held the ring, thinking about one of the few memories she still had of her mother.

Eight-year-old Mary had skinned her knee and was crying, and her mother inspected the bruise. Her mother cupped her hands gently over the knee. Mary could feel the heat from her mother's hands healing her. The antique wedding ring on her mother's left hand seemed to twinkle at Mary as her mother closed her eyes and held that position. After a few moments of silence, her mother opened her eyes, kissed the injured knee, and said, "It's going to be all right, little angel."

The jewelry store owner arrived from the back room. "Hi, I'm Mr. Jankowitz." He held out his hand to shake Mary's.

"I'm Mary. Nice to meet you." She shook his hand, noticing that it was soft and meaty with a loose grip. Her daddy had always told her how important it was to have a firm grip. "Be wary of a man with a limp handshake," he used to tell her.

"So, Eva said you're interested in selling this ring."

"Yes, if the price is right."

"You don't seem too keen on selling it."

Mary shrunk a little, wondering how he knew.

"I saw the way you were looking at the ring when I came out. We have women in here who can't wait to get rid of their wedding rings after a nasty divorce. Other people have no emotional attachment to the jewelry they wish to sell. You, however, look like you're giving up something important to you. Have you considered pawning it instead?"

Mary squirmed and her cheeks turned red. She viewed pawnshops as being a last resort for people who were financially desperate. "I already tried pawning it, to be honest. They didn't offer me enough. I know what it's worth, so I decided selling it would be better."

Mr. Jankowitz picked up Mary's mother's ring and looked at it through his jeweler's loupe. A minute later, he put it down. "What do you think it's worth, Mary?"

"I'd rather you told me. You're the expert." Mary recalled how her daddy, a car salesman his entire adult life, had taught her never to be the first to name a price in a negotiation.

"I can give you nine hundred dollars for it right now," Mr. Jankowitz said.

"I know it's worth twenty-seven hundred, at least," replied Mary. She was grateful for the negotiation skills her daddy had taught her. Most people would never know to triple the starting price the other party suggested.

"It may be worth that, but I have to turn a profit. Otherwise what's the point? You have to understand I'm in business to make money."

Mary picked up the ring from the glass case and placed it back in the box that she'd brought it in. Her daddy had taught her always to make a gesture to show you're willing to walk away. Since she'd come to Mr. Jankowitz to sell her ring, boxing the ring would help to diminish any belief he might have that she was desperate to sell, even though she really was.

"Two thousand two hundred," she said. "You'll make five hundred, and we both know this will sell quickly."

Mr. Jankowitz stared blankly while his mind was thinking. Then he said, "You never know if something will sell quickly, dear. Trust me, I've made that mistake too many times in the last thirty years. I can go as high as fifteen hundred in cash right now." He looked at Eva. "Do we have fifteen hundred in the cash register?"

Eva opened the cash register and lifted the inside drawer to count the large bills under it. "Yes we do, Mr. Jankowitz."

"Two thousand one hundred," said Mary with a quiver to her voice. She knew that was how much they needed to pay three months of back rent. Her daddy had also always taught her to make an offer and then say nothing, so she bit her tongue even though her impulse was to keep talking.

Mr. Jankowitz's demeanor quickly changed. He wanted the ring, and he felt the pressure Mary was putting on him. He wasn't used to skilled negotiators, and he didn't like it. He was now standing tall with his arms crossed over his puffed-up chest, partly out of frustration and partly to try to intimidate Mary. "I'll give you one thousand eight hundred and not one penny more," he said, adding, "The only reason I'm willing to go that high is because I believe I have someone in mind who might be interested in this. That's my final offer. You can either take it or leave it."

Mary leaned on the counter to stop her hands from shaking. She couldn't believe she'd gotten this skilled businessman to increase his offer from nine hundred to eighteen hundred dollars. Her only hesitancy was that she really needed twenty-one hundred. She and Robby had no other way of earning the rest of the cash they needed unless Robby got a new client or she found a new job, which was unlikely to happen before the next month's rent was due.

She was about to say yes when she looked down at her mother's ring. Thinking about how it was the last memento she had of her, she began to cry. She picked up the ring and held it, perhaps for the final time, and was flooded with emotion.

Mr. Jankowitz looked over at Eva and shrugged his shoulders as if to say, *What is this all about?*

Eva, now misty-eyed herself, walked over to Mr. Jankowitz and whispered, "It's the ring of her mother, who died when Mary was ten."

Mary wanted to take the money, but no words would come out of her mouth to finalize the deal. Every time she tried, she began to sob and shake.

"Listen, young lady," began Mr. Jankowitz, "my offer stands for exactly a week. Go home and think about it. If you want to sell the ring, you have until Tuesday. You're a good negotiator; I'll give you that. The truth is I'm offering you more than I should be offering. Nonetheless, I'll give you a week or the deal's off."

Mary put the box in her purse and thanked them both while also apologizing for her crying and indecisiveness. She then rushed out of the store in a fit of tears.

When the door closed, Eva shot Mr. Jankowitz a look of contempt. "You couldn't have been a little more compassionate? The poor girl's selling her dead mother's ring, and you have to play hardball with her?"

Eva sighed and stormed into the back room.

CHAPTER THREE:

THE AWAKENING

ROBBY DROPPED by the sports memorabilia shop owned by his friend Matt Mooney. He wanted to ask Matt what he could get for the hockey puck signed by Wayne Gretzky.

The store was filled with customers: a boy looking at baseball cards covered in acrylic cases, a woman holding a football signed by Drew Bledsoe, a man admiring an aerial view of Fenway Park.

Matt stood behind the counter waiting for the boy looking at baseball cards to make a decision. His six-foot-three, 220-pound muscular frame intimidated most would-be shoplifters. He hadn't been much smaller in high school when he and Robby hung out, which was why Matt played football. After high school, he got into weight lifting. Now he had trouble finding shirts with sleeves that fit his arms. Robby called him Mr. Clean because he shaved his blond head to hide his thinning hair, making him look like the cartoon guy from the Procter & Gamble commercials.

When the boy left, Matt introduced himself to the woman who had been patiently waiting and holding a football. "Hi, I'm Matt Mooney." He held his hand out.

The woman shook his hand. "Ruth Horowitz," she said. "Nice to meet you, Matt. I'm thinking about buying this for my nephew. It's his twelfth birthday, but, to be honest, I don't even know if he follows football."

"Do you know what teams he might wear on his shirts or baseball caps?"

Ruth sighed. "No. It's not something I notice."

Robby, standing behind her and overhearing their conversation, asked, "Do you have any pictures of him on your phone?"

She pulled her phone out and began searching through the photographs. "Here's one. Can you make out the team on his tee shirt?" She held the phone up so Robby could see it.

Robby smiled. "The Boston Bruins."

"Really?" she said, relieved.

"He would know," said Matt. "It's his favorite team."

She looked at Matt. "Do you have any Bruins memorabilia?"

Matt walked Ruth over to the corner of the store where all his hockey products were displayed, and Ruth began combing through the Bruins merchandise.

"Pick a few in your budget and I'll help you choose what I think a twelve-year-old is apt to like," Matt told her as he walked back to the counter where Robby waited.

"Hey, Dogbreath," he said, putting his large arm around Robby's shoulders. "Thanks for the help. I never would have thought of asking for photos." He saw the Gretzky-signed puck on the counter. "You don't want to sell this, do you? Didn't you catch it at a game with your dad?"

Robby scoffed. "Yeah, but that's no big deal. It's been sitting in a box in the attic, so I thought I might as well get some cash for it."

"Sure, but this is a nice memory. You used to be a huge Gretzky fan. He even signed it with a white marker. You should keep this in your office, man."

"It's just more clutter. I already have enough clutter in my office."

It was all lies. Robby hated selling that puck, but he wasn't going to let on to Matt that he needed the money. Matt was a mega-successful storeowner. He now had stores in New Hampshire and Connecticut in addition to this Massachusetts location. Worse, he had invited Robby to be his partner when he opened the first store five years ago, but Robby had wanted to be a writer. It was too embarrassing to let Matt know that he was broke when Matt's business was thriving.

After looking it up in a book, Matt told him, "I can give you two hundred and fifty bucks for the puck. I might only break even on it, but I'll try selling it for three hundred fifty. I might get lucky if the right person comes in here. But let's be honest, it's not like New England is the best place to sell a Gretzky puck."

"Is that really the best you can do?"

"I just told you, dude. I'll probably only break even." Matt stood in thought for a moment. "Hey, didn't you have a photo of Gretzky holding the puck after he signed it?"

Robby was surprised Matt remembered it. "Yeah, but I have no idea where that went. The last I recall, it was on a wall in my father's office."

"Well, Dipstick, that would raise the value of this thing. It's proof that the Great One really signed it. Get that and I'll give you three hundred and fifty bucks."

"Okay, I'll ask my father about it. I'm off to visit him now. He's over at Saint Vincent's hospital again."

"Again? How's he doing?" asked Matt. "Didn't he have like half a lung removed or something?"

"Yeah, a few years ago. He's doing okay. He has pneumonia again though, for a third time. Nothing he hasn't beaten before."

"Tell him I said hello, will ya?"

"Of course. Talk to you later, Matt."

Robby stuffed the puck in his pocket and left for the hospital, which was only fifteen minutes away. During the drive, he had an ache in his stomach. The more he thought about selling the puck, the worse his stomachache got. Still, he was tired of eating boxed macaroni and cheese, which was practically all he and Mary could afford. Selling it was the right decision. He turned on the radio and found a talk show in order to distract himself from his thoughts.

Minutes later, Robby walked through the doors to the hospital. He was immediately greeted by the smell of bleach, stale air, and body odor. *I hate this place*, he thought. *I hate the smell, the fluorescent lighting, the atmosphere of sickness and death. How can Dad stand it? It's reason enough to stay healthy.*

He took the elevator to his father's third-floor ward. His father had been in and out of there so often that the nurses at the main desk greeted Robby by name.

"Hi, Robby. Dave's waiting for you."

"Hi, Betsy. Hi, Sarah. Hi, Paula. Thanks."

Robby walked into Room 305 and saw his father sitting on the edge of his bed looking out the window. He looked like an older James Dean. Robby hadn't visited in a while. It was too depressing for him. His father used to be such a figure of strength to Robby. He had been charismatic and successful. He had once owned an advertising agency that gave him the freedom to do whatever he wanted, so he taught philosophy at the local college. He had a master's degree in philosophy. Now the agency was gone, he no longer taught at the college, and he looked frail and weak in his pajamas. His hair was disheveled and gray, and his skin was pale from not seeing the sun in too long.

"Hey, Dad. You miss it?"

"Huh?" Dave was startled out of his stupor. "Hey there, Robby. What's that you said?"

"I noticed you were looking outside. You miss it?"

"Oh yeah. I'm trying to remember what it's like to breathe fresh air."

Robby walked over to the bed, and the two men embraced.

"Where's Mary today?" Dave asked.

"She was grocery shopping, so I decided to head over myself. She doesn't even know I'm here."

"Oh, okay. So how's work, son? What are you writing these days?"

"Nothing at the moment. I'm in a bit of a dry spell, although I do have two prospective clients who both want their autobiographies written. If I land just one of them, I'll be busy for at least six months. One of them is the actor Dale Davenport."

"Dale Davenport, huh? I liked that movie he was in where he went undercover in the motorcycle gang. But I thought you were tired of writing other people's books. You said you wanted to write your own books."

Robby looked down. "This is what pays the bills. At least it *was* paying the bills. Maybe it's the economy or something, but the clients just aren't coming like they did the first couple of years I was in this business. The same two prospects have been thinking about hiring me for almost two months now. Meanwhile, my bills aren't getting paid."

"I wish I could help you out, son. But these hospital bills have damned near cleaned me out. I still can't believe I stopped paying my health insurance. For a period there, as you know, I just kind of let everything fall by the wayside."

"I couldn't accept your money even if you had it to give, Dad. I'm old enough now that I shouldn't need you to pay my bills for me. I just don't understand why the clients aren't coming like they used to."

"Maybe it's because your heart isn't in ghostwriting anymore. Ever think of that?"

"You don't get it, Dad. It's not easy making a living as a writer, especially writing fiction."

"You're right. What do I know about the book publishing business? One thing I do know, though, is that some people make a damned good living writing fiction. So I'd be cautious with that limiting belief you keep affirming."

"I know. You're right. We're going to be fine. I shouldn't have said anything." Robby looked around to find a way to change the subject. "Hey, do you want me to get a wheelchair and take you out to the courtyard? It's beautiful outside."

Dave agreed and began to put on a robe that was draped across the bottom of his bed. He had no sooner finished putting the robe over his pajamas when Robby arrived back with a wheelchair he had found just outside the door. Dave was anxious to get outside the hospital walls.

"That was quick. It's nice to be young and healthy, huh?"

Robby didn't answer. He felt his father was responsible for his own poor health because he didn't take good care of himself anymore. Robby helped his dad from the bed to the wheelchair, and they made the trip down the elevator to the outside courtyard. Robby pushed the wheelchair next to a concrete bench so he could sit next to his father. As soon as they arrived, his father flipped the foot pedals of the wheelchair out of the way and lit up a cigarette that he had hidden in his robe pocket.

Robby rolled his eyes; smoking was why his father had needed lung surgery in the first place. His father noticed Robby's gesture and lifted his eyebrows as he glared at his son.

"Son, a long time ago I chose quality over quantity. It's one of the few pleasures I have in life anymore. Just allow me this without making me feel bad every time I light up, okay?"

Robby nodded, unable to look at his father. "Okay, Dad. I'm sorry."

There was an awkward silence.

"It's nice out here, huh, Dad?"

The sunlight was beating down on Dave. He closed his eyes and turned his face toward the sun. "There's really nothing like the early summer sun on your skin." There was a long pause before he added, "So what's going on? I'm not sure you've ever visited me in the middle of the day before, and certainly not without Mary. Is there something you want to talk about?"

Robby looked at his father. "Am I that transparent? Actually, there are two things. I was cleaning out the attic today when I came across an old cigar box of yours. I must have packed it with my own stuff accidentally when I moved out of your house. Anyway, it had this in it. I thought I'd drop it off." Robby handed his father the mala beads.

"Oh wow, wow, wow. I haven't seen these in years." Dave stared at the mala with a grin as he slowly moved each of the beads between the thumb and index finger of his right hand. He studied each bead while Robby watched him with curiosity.

"I had no idea how important they were to you," said Robby. "I'm glad I brought them. They came with this little booklet." He pulled the booklet out of his pocket and placed it on his father's leg.

"Oh good, you have that, too. Have you read the manual?"

"You mean this tiny booklet? I only read the first paragraph. It seemed kind of new agey—you know, woo-woo."

"No, no, no. There's nothing woo-woo about it. Practicing the mala is an ancient spiritual ritual. It's sacred in the Buddhist and Hindu religions, but nonreligious people love mala beads, too, for their beauty, history, and function. What do you want to know about them?"

"I don't know that I want to know anything. I guess you could tell me what kind of stones those are."

"These beads are made of lapis, which is almost always this royal blue color with gold flecks. Mala beads can be made of many different types of stones or other materials, like wood, seeds, or bone. Every person attracts the perfect stone or material for what he needs because mala beads hold an energetic property that strengthens energy centers within the owner. Do you like the color and appearance of these mala beads?"

"I think the beads are gorgeous, especially because they're this particular shade of blue. Of course, I've always been attracted to anything blue. Hence the blue shirt I'm wearing, my blue pickup, and my blue sneakers." Robby laughed. "Mary thinks I need to expand my repertoire to other colors."

"Well then, the lapis mala is perfect for you. I did a lot of research on this stone. The full name is lapis lazuli, which means 'blue stone.' *Lapis* in Latin means 'stone,' and *lazuli* comes from the Persian word *lazhward*, which means 'blue.' It symbolizes wisdom and truth. The ancient Egyptians considered the gold flecks in the stone stars in the evening sky. They would meditate on these flecks to engage mystical forces that they believed could transform their lives. Still, in many cultures worldwide, lapis is believed to stimulate our ability to acquire knowledge, truth, and understanding. It's the perfect stone for writers, so I'm not surprised it came into your life."

Dave handed the mala back to Robby. Robby leaned away from his father, refusing to take it. "No, Dad, it's yours. You keep it. I don't believe in that kind of stuff. You know that."

"Actually, Robby, it's yours now. It found you. If a mala comes into your life that's not being used by someone else, it is meant to be yours. That's a very special mala. It has much to teach you."

"Teach me?" Robby sneered. "How can a string of beads teach me something?"

"Don't mock what you don't understand, son. I'm serious. Take it."

Realizing his father meant it, Robby held out his hand. His father dropped the mala into his palm.

"I remember placing that in the cigar box many years ago," his father said. "It had taught me all it had to teach me, or so I thought at the time. I guess I was young and arrogant once, too."

Robby ignored the comment. He was used to his father throwing little wisecracks his way, half kidding and half serious. "The manual called it a *magic* mala. You don't believe in magic, do you, Dad?" he asked.

"I don't believe in magic," Dave replied. "Still, what I learned from that mala is without a doubt magical, although not in a hocus-pocus kind of way. Everything that mala taught me is about the natural ways of the Universe. You see, Creative Intelligence, the Source, or whatever you want to call the higher power, is in constant communication with us. And we're in constant communication with it."

"It? Don't you mean Him, Dad, as in God?"

"I say 'it' because the higher power I believe in isn't male or female, it's both. In fact, the higher power I've come to know is more an energy than some old guy in the sky."

"Does that mean you don't believe in God anymore?"

"Quite the contrary. I believe in God as much as anyone. I just recognize that God isn't separate from us. By realizing God is everywhere and not just some old man in the clouds who is separate from us, I recognize God as the oneness of the Universe that connects everyone and everything. In this way, it's easier to understand God by thinking of it as energy. And since we all have so many learned conceptions about a God that is separate from us, I prefer to call God 'Creative Intelligence.' For me, this more accurately describes God as our Creator, which is also the Intelligence of the Universe. Sometimes I just refer to it as 'the Universe.'"

Robby thought about it and nodded in agreement. "I like that. That makes sense to me."

Dave took a slow drag on his cigarette and exhaled as he continued. "Creative Intelligence is the energy of love, wisdom, and creativity. Because you and I come from this powerful creative force, we too are powerful creative beings. However, most people don't know how to utilize their own creative abilities, which is what the mala teaches."

A butterfly fluttered over Dave's robe and landed on the left sleeve, directly between the two men. Dave and Robby paused in awe of the insect's grace and beauty. A minute later, after it had fluttered away, the father and son looked at each other in amazement.

"See, son? That's the Universe's way of getting our attention. It's called coincidence. This is one of the four ways Creative Intelligence communicates with us. It's attempting to bring our focus into the present moment to emphasize that our conversation is important."

"Wow, Dad, you're freaking me out here. I've never heard you talk like this before. I didn't know you were so religious."

"I'm not talking about religion. I'm talking about the place where science and spirituality meet. Some call it *metaphysics*. Others even call it *being spiritual but not religious*. Whatever you choose to call it, we're all connected to an invisible force of infinite creation, although only a few people are aware of it and even fewer know how it works."

Robby was now wide-eyed and sitting up straight on the concrete bench. At that moment, a crow landed on a birdbath in front of them for about fifteen seconds. The crow cawed and then flew away.

Robby turned to his father with a look of surprise and said, "Well, that was weird." He shook his head from side to side and then continued. "I must admit, you've made me curious. Is this knowledge how you accumulated all your wealth, Dad?" He blushed a little after he said it.

Dave blew out a puff of smoke as he laughed. His shoulders dropped, his head cocked to the side, and he took in a deep breath of fresh air while trying to decide how to answer the question. Then he said, "Yes, Robby, the mala taught me how to use the creative force to attract wealth. There's no question about that. Yet it taught me a lot more than that.

"The mala also taught me how to create good relationships, how to recognize the blessings in my life, how to make the best of my circumstances regardless of what happens, and how to attain inner peace in a chaotic world. Money is wonderful, and our accumulation of money is a fine way to monitor our success at using our own powers of creation, but money is merely one of life's unlimited gifts that we can use the mala to attain."

Robby's mind was racing. "Why haven't you told me this stuff before?"

"Well, one reason is that you never asked."

"I never knew to ask. I never knew you had this knowledge."

Dave stared at a pink rose growing next to him in the courtyard. "That's half the problem. We don't know what we don't know."

"Yeah, I guess that's it. So where do we begin? My mind is filling up with questions."

Dave looked Robby straight in the eyes. "I'll tell you what. You take that mala home, read the manual, and follow the steps it gives you. After you've done what the manual teaches, I'll answer any questions you have. Deal?"

"Okay, that's a deal," said Robby.

Dave took one last puff, then crushed the cigarette butt between his thick, tobacco-stained fingers so it turned into tiny little bits of tobacco that disappeared as he sprinkled them into the dirt below his wheel-chair. He took the filter and whatever white paper was left and dropped it into his cigarette pack, then stuffed the pack into his robe pocket.

"Now get me back inside, Robby. All this fresh air might kill me," he said with a chuckle. He put his feet on the pedals and tapped the side of the chair to signal he was ready. "Take me to my castle!" he ordered playfully.

Robby pushed him forward, and the glass doors opened automatically. As they entered the hospital, Robby's senses were once again filled with the institutional odors and lighting he so despised.

Back at Room 305, Dave slowly and painfully crawled off the wheel-chair and back into bed with Robby's assistance. Once his father was settled, Robby pulled out the hockey puck from his jacket pocket. "Remember this, Dad?" Robby handed the puck to Dave.

Dave's eyes became misty the moment he saw it. He took it from Robby and held it in his hand, admiring it. "That brings back memories. I'll never forget that night. We had fun, didn't we?"

"We sure did. We ate pizza between periods and you gave me a sip of your beer."

Dave laughed. "That's right. I remember you almost choked."

"It wasn't as good as everyone made it seem."

Dave handed the puck back to Robby.

"I remember you took a picture of me and Gretzky that night," said Robby. "I think it used to be on the wall across from your desk. Do you know where that is now?"

Dave was silent for a moment, staring into nowhere. Then he looked at Robby. "I think that's in a frame in the basement, still in front of my desk. You should definitely get that and put it in your house. It's good to have things around that remind you of good times. You still have a key, right?"

"Yes, on my key chain."

"Well, water the plants while you're there, will you? I don't think my neighbor gets to it often enough."

Robby stood up and put on his jacket to signal he was leaving. "By the way, my friend Matt says hello."

The two men hugged before Robby headed toward the door.

"Matt, he's the big one. He's a nice kid. I always liked him. I used to run into him every now and then. Guess I haven't been getting out like I used to."

"Well, he's thirty-two now, just like me."

Dave laughed. "You'll both always be kids to me." He added, "Make sure to bring that lovely wife of yours next time, okay?"

"Okay, Dad. I'll see you soon," Robby said as he left the room. He couldn't wait to get out of the building.

CHAPTER FOUR

THE TRUTH

ROBBY HEADED for the library on his way home from the hospital to read the booklet entitled *Your New Mala Manual*. He didn't want Mary to see him reading anything new age. She might jump to conclusions and get excited.

Mary had tried to have spiritual discussions with him in the past, and Robby always shut her down. After a while she just stopped trying. He felt a bit hypocritical reading about the mala, but he liked his father's description of it as a process where science and spirituality meet. He wasn't ready to accept anything new age or woo-woo, but he felt that he could at least consider something called metaphysics.

Since his father was at St. Vincent's Hospital on Vernon Street, Robby swung over to the Worcester Library on Salem Street, only minutes away. He pulled into the parking lot and looked under the seats of his pickup truck for some change to put in the parking meter. He found a rollerball pen that was his favorite kind, the post office box key he thought he had lost, and four quarters and a dime. *Just enough for an hour of parking*, he thought. *That should be plenty of time to read a tiny booklet.*

Upon entering, the smell of the library, in stark contrast to that of the hospital, was a welcome aroma. Robby loved the scent of old books. He took a slow, deep breath through his nostrils and then found a seat at a table in the anthropology section where there wasn't another person in sight. He pulled out the manual and began reading where he'd left off in the attic.

> *Traditionally, the proper way to hold a mala is with your right hand. Beginning with the first bead, pull each bead toward you, one at a time, with your thumb and index finger.*

Checking that no one was nearby, Robby pulled the mala beads out of his pocket and tried following the instructions. It took a bit of effort and concentration, but he soon got the hang of moving from bead to bead using just his thumb and index finger.

He continued reading.

> *There are 108 beads plus one extra bead commonly known as the "guru" bead that indicates the beginning and end point of the mala. The significance of the number 108 is that the 1 signifies the Creator and higher truth, the 0 signifies emptiness or the space between our thoughts and breaths, and the 8 signifies infinity, timelessness, and eternity.*
>
> *Begin by setting an intention for your mala session. What do you wish to communicate to your higher power? Do you wish to communicate an object or outcome you would like to create or attract into your life?*
>
> *Here are some examples of intentions you might set.*
>
> *I would like to attract more money into my life*
> *I would like to attract a fulfilling and prosperous new job*

I would like to create better health in my body
I would like to create more harmony and romance with my
spouse
I would like to attract new friends, or a new lover
I would like to feel greater inner peace
I would like to feel more joy
I would like to increase my level of physical fitness

There was a tiny pencil on the table, like the ones golfers use, alongside a sheet of blank paper from the copy machine. Someone must have left them lying there after copying a page from a book. Robby turned the sheet of paper over and used the pencil to write his intention on it. He wrote the first example at the top: "I would like to attract more money into my life." He then read more of the manual.

> *Turn this intention into a brief mantra, usually only a few words long, which you will use to represent your intention.*

> *Here are a few examples of mantras you might try.*

> *I am tapped into an infinite supply of abundance*
> *I enjoy loving relationships in my life*
> *I am healthy and filled with vitality*
> *I love life and life loves me*
> *Every day, in every way, I'm getting fitter and fitter*
> *I am grateful for all the blessings in my life*
> *I am fearless*
> *I am deserving of wealth, health, and happiness*

Under his intention, Robby wrote down one of the examples given, "I am deserving of wealth, health, and happiness," but he wasn't satisfied with it. He crossed it out and then wrote his own intention:

"Money comes easily to me." He liked his mantra and thought, *I'm good at this.* Then he continued reading the manual.

There are many Buddhist and Hindu mantras that you can memorize that have been used for thousands of years. What's important is that you understand their intentions even if you don't know the meaning of every word.

The language of Sanskrit is based more on energy than meaning, so each word carries an energy vibration. Therefore, each word grows in power as it vibrates from your vocal cords, attracting to you a frequency match that you project outwardly as you speak it. Here's a popular Hindu abundance mantra in the Sanskrit language.

Om Shrim Maha Lakshmiyei Swaha.

It is pronounced: Om Shreem maah-hah lahk-shmee-yay swah-hah.

Om *is how every mantra begins.* Shrim *is the seed sound for abundance.* Maha *means "great," and in this case it means "a lot of abundance."* Lakshmi *is the goddess of abundance and receiving. The "yei" is an activating sound, so chanting* "Lakshmi-yei" *activates the Lakshmi within us. And* swaha *is like* maha *but signifies respect, so it means "the Great One" in reference to Lakshmi.*

Ultimately the mantra means you are showing deep respect to the goddess of abundance, Lakshmi, for the great quantity of abundance she has sent your way.

Robby was amused by the reference to the Great One since Wayne Gretzky also had been given that name. *That's a neat coincidence,* he thought to himself. "Gretzky swaha," he said out loud with a chuckle.

He liked the idea of using an ancient mantra for abundance. He thought it might have a greater impact because of its powerful energy vibration. *It must work because it has been around for thousands of years,* Robby thought, then pondered, *Would people keep using it if it wasn't effective?* He decided he would use this mantra instead of the one he himself created to begin his mala practice. He liked the way it rolled off his tongue. Although he still felt slightly skeptical, he was desperate enough to open his mind to new possibilities.

> *Now say your mantra aloud while thinking about its intention for every one of the 108 beads of your mala. In this way, you are repeating and contemplating your intention 108 times, which will take you approximately ten minutes each session, give or take a few minutes.*
>
> *This exercise is a powerful method for communicating your desires to Creative Intelligence. Few people take the time to do this. Imagine doing this exercise twice daily. Imagine how much creative power twenty-plus minutes of intention setting a day will accomplish. Few people know how life changing this exercise is because most people do the exact opposite.*

As he read further in the manual, Robby suddenly became aware of somebody sitting directly across the table from him, a petite blond woman just a little younger than he, and she was staring right at him. He couldn't ignore the energy of her gaze, so he looked up from reading his mala manual. The woman's entire face was smiling: her lips, her cheeks, her eyes, her nose, and even her ears seemed to beam with joy.

She appeared to have no discomfort staring at a stranger and interrupting his reading.

"I love mala beads," she began with no formal introduction. She appeared happy and vital and spoke very quickly. "I've been using mala beads since I was eight."

Robby realized his mala was in plain sight. *It's like having dog treats at the park*, he thought, amusing himself. *She must have been drawn to it from across the room.*

"I have seven. My first one is made of red jasper. My second one, which was a gift, is tiger's eye. My third one I saw at a store and just had to have it. That one is citrine. I won my fourth mala, which has jade beads, in a raffle. My fifth one is aquamarine. My sixth one is amethyst. And my seventh one I just bought yesterday. It's clear quartz. Every time I grow personally and spiritually, I find myself acquiring a new mala. I love yours. It's lapis, right?"

Robby was slightly resentful of the disturbance, but the young woman's enthusiasm was infectious. She seemed so happy that he had a mala that he didn't want to ruin it for her.

"Umm, yes, lapis, I guess. It used to be my father's. I just found it in the attic."

"So it's yours now," she interrupted. "It adopted you."

"Yeah, that's exactly what my father said."

"I'm sorry. I didn't even introduce myself. I got excited seeing you with your mala. My name is Tru."

"Tru as in Trudy?"

"No, Tru as in Truth," she said. Then she rambled, "My parents were sort of hippies. They named me Truth, but people call me Tru. My younger sister is named Freedom. We call her Free. And my older brother is named Alchemy. We just call him Al." The last abbreviation made them both laugh.

"That's kind of cool. I'm Robert, but people call me Robby."

"Nice to meet you, Robby. Is this your first mala?"

"Yeah. I just found it this morning," he said shyly.

"I'm so excited for you. My malas have completely changed my life—for the better, of course. They've taught me that I'm always guided."

"Guided?"

"Sure, by my spiritual guides. Or you might call them guardian angels. I like to talk a lot. You probably noticed." She giggled. "So when nobody is around, I know I can talk to my spirit guides—my guardian angels—who I believe work with God. I know they hear me. My malas taught me that."

"I've never been religious," said Robby. "My mother was. Tell me, how do you know your guides hear you?" Although he didn't believe in fanciful beings like angels and spirit guides, he was curious how she would answer. He had often teased his wife for holding similar beliefs.

"Because they answer me, silly! I ask for guidance, and they always give it to me—usually through my intuition. There are other ways, but my intuition is pretty strong. It got a lot stronger after I began working with a mala."

Tru continued talking even though Robby didn't respond. He really didn't have an opportunity to speak.

"You don't have to talk out loud like I do for your guides to respond. I only talk out loud to my guides when I'm alone. Still, everyone is talking with their spiritual guides all the time with just their thoughts, which is why we all have to be super careful about what we think. Did you know every thought sends out a signal that God responds to in kind?"

"I'm not sure I understand," admitted Robby.

"We're sort of like magnets that attract whatever we think about. So if you think happy thoughts, you'll attract happy people and circumstances into your life. If you think unhappy thoughts, you'll attract unhappy people and circumstances into your life."

Robby reflected that his father often said things like this—about attraction—but he had never paid attention. Maybe there was something to it. He considered the idea of the mind being a magnetic beacon attracting whatever it was thinking about. If that was, in fact, the case, he would need to be more careful.

"Is that true, Tru?" Robby realized he'd said "true-Tru" and found it amusing. Tru didn't seem to notice. She was probably used to it.

"Uh-huh, totally. Most people complain about their troubles or talk to others about what worries them most of the time, which communicates to God that this is what they wish to expand upon in their lives. Anything we focus upon expands. So it's best to focus on what we want rather than what we don't want in our lives."

"What we focus upon expands?"

"It sure does. Some people think about what they want but then follow that thought up with an opposing thought that they are undeserving of it or not lucky enough to have it."

"I do that sometimes," Robby admitted.

"Or they express thoughts of disbelief that they are capable of attracting such outcomes into their lives. If we communicate what we want, but then spend equal time communicating why we won't get it, the negative communication cancels out the positive one. This is why the power of your belief plays such a big role in attraction."

Robby wasn't sure what to think of this fast-talking young woman exploding with enthusiasm, but everything she said strongly resonated with him. He knew that he was the type of person who held thoughts of worry and fear in his mind more than positive thoughts of hope and optimism, especially lately. Because his life wasn't going so great, he had been worrying a lot more in the last month or two.

He also knew he was the kind of person who would follow up a positive thought with something negative like *That never happens to me* or *I'm never lucky like that.* He was amazed how much this stranger was speaking directly to him as if she could see inside of him. He remained silent and kept listening.

Tru picked up Robby's mala and looked at it while she talked. "The mala is an awesome tool for teaching us how to think more consciously. It gives you the opportunity to repeat your desires for divine creation 108 times without allowing space or time for opposing thoughts. By repeating your mantra over and over again, there is no time or space in your mind for anything other than thoughts of your desired intention. And if you do this twice a day—morning and night—you have just doubled the power that the mala grants you. It's a great way to begin and end your day."

Tru handed the lapis mala back to Robby, and he stared at it with amazement as she continued. "The Universe does not know the difference between positive and negative, good or bad. It only knows how to respond to the energy frequency that you send it. Your thoughts are energy that vibrate at a specific frequency; every thought holds a different frequency. And when you speak your thoughts out loud, the sound of your voice gives it more power energetically."

Robby thought about the sound of Tru's voice as she kept talking. There was something unusual about it. It was like it had a musical tone to it, almost like the sound of wind chimes touching.

"God sends you a frequency match to whatever you have requested in your thoughts," she said. "Think of wealth, and God delivers wealth. Think of financial struggle, and God delivers financial struggle. Think of health, love, joy, illness, loneliness, or sadness, and that is exactly what will be delivered to you."

Robby remembered a time when he was angry about something a client had said on the telephone and then he'd driven to the store immediately after the upsetting phone call. On that trip to the store, he was pulled over by the police for failure to use his turn signal, he was cut off by another driver who stole his intended parking spot, and he ended up with a nasty cashier who got impatient with him when he used coins to pay for the milk. And that wasn't the only time negative events had piled up on him. He had recognized years ago that bad things tended to occur whenever he was in a lousy mood. Now this sprightly woman was explaining why that happened.

Tru was bursting with energy. She was kneeling on the chair and talking with her hands. "Want to know a life-changing secret?" she asked Robby.

"Sure."

"Not many people know this one. If there are aspects of your life that bring you happiness and pleasure, then send God the signal that you are grateful for them. Gratitude is one of the most powerful frequencies in the Universe. The best way to do this is to create a mantra of gratitude to use with your mala," she said.

Tru grabbed Robby's pencil and paper on the table and began writing on it. "Here's a powerful mantra you can use. I created it for myself." She wrote it down as she said it aloud: "Thank you for the blessings." She looked up at Robby to make sure he was paying attention. "When you say it, think of a blessing in your life for which you feel grateful. I'll give you some examples. Say thank you for the blessings and think of your health. Say thank you for the blessings and think of your family. Say thank you for the blessings and think of your home. Say thank you for the blessings and think of your friends. Say thank you for the blessings and think of your writing talent."

"Wait!" Robby stopped her. "How'd you know I have a talent for writing?"

"Just a hunch. Like I said, my intuition is really strong. Plus, lapis is often the stone of writers or lawyers, and you don't seem like a lawyer." She snorted as she laughed.

Robby's mind was blown away by Tru's ability to know he was a writer, but her snort made him laugh, and distracted him from thinking too deeply about it.

"So while practicing your mala with the gratitude mantra," said Tru, her whole body squirming from her passion, "you will think of 108 blessings in your life. And by doing this exercise, you are communicating to God—through your spiritual guides, if you prefer—that you want more of these things. It's like saying, 'This is what I like in my life, God. Please keep it coming.' And God will deliver more of every blessing that makes you feel grateful."

Robby couldn't deny it. This was all making perfect sense to him. It was almost scientific, like his father had said: "It's not about luck or what you deserve; it's about sending out an energetic frequency, which the Universe responds to in kind." The idea reminded Robby of fishing. *You wouldn't use a saltwater lure when fishing for a freshwater fish*, he thought to himself. *Likewise, you shouldn't complain about your life all day and expect good things to come your way.*

Robby totally understood what Tru had explained about gratitude, too. He knew that when people thanked him for a kind deed he had done for them, their gratitude made him want to do more for them. He had always thought that it was interesting how people's gratitude toward him made him want to give them more. So why wouldn't God respond the same way? It made perfect sense.

The librarian walked by and overheard Tru talking. She approached Robby and Tru. "I'm going to have to ask you to lower your voices a little," she said softly.

They both apologized. When the librarian turned the corner and was out of sight, Tru stood up. "I have to go anyway," she said in a loud whisper, still not very quietly. "One last thing. If you think, say, or write something negative, something that you are worried about or complaining about, quickly offset that energy frequency by rethinking, restating, or rewriting the thought in the positive.

"And if you act in such a way that is in conflict with your intention—such as setting an intention to attract new friends but then refusing to go to a party when you are invited—this is the same as thinking or writing in the negative. Actions are just thoughts in practice. So always make sure your thoughts, words, and actions are in alignment with your intentions.

"And now I really have to go." Tru started walking away.

Robby noticed she seemed to bounce when she walked. Everything about her seemed light and filled with positive vigor.

"Nice to meet you, Robby!" she said rather loudly as she waved goodbye with both hands.

"Nice to meet you, Truth."

Robby heard what he'd said again and thought, *Truth just gave me a lesson on the mala.* He was somewhat freaked out by what had just happened. It almost didn't feel real. He looked at the paper where Tru had written "Thank you for the blessings," which confirmed the encounter was real. After absorbing everything she'd taught him, he picked up the tiny mala manual to finish reading it before he had to leave.

A common practice to begin is to choose a mantra that you will repeat with every bead on your mala twice daily, in the morning and in the evening, and do this for forty days.

If possible, track your results in a journal or diary. At the end of forty days, change the mantra to something new and commit to another forty-day cycle. If you do, your life will never be the same.

In summary, decide upon an intention, an outcome you wish to create in your life, such as wealth, health, joy, friendship, love, or career success—the possibilities are infinite. Next, create a mantra that represents your intention. Next, repeat your mantra 108 times while holding each bead of the mala between your thumb and index finger. Think of your intention when you say your mantra. Do this in the morning and in the evening. For best results, commit to working with one mantra twice daily for forty days. Record the results daily.

So much of everything he was learning made complete sense to Robby despite his skepticism. Like his father said, the mala beads seemed to represent an intersection where science met spirituality. He decided to commit to a daily practice of using his strand of mala beads with the Sanskrit abundance mantra twice a day for forty days.

Why not? It won't make things worse, he thought. *And maybe this will help my life improve, if even just a little.*

He decided to begin the next day. He knew he'd have to find a private place to practice his mala exercise where no one would see him. He felt lighter just having made the commitment. He packed up his mala, the manual, and his piece of paper and left the library to go home to Mary.

CHAPTER FIVE:
THE WAKE-UP CALL

BAM, **BAM**, BAM!
Mary woke up from a deep sleep to a loud knock on the door.

BAM, BAM, BAM!

"Robby?" she yelled. "Robby? Are you home?"

She didn't like answering the door when someone arrived unexpectedly, especially first thing in the morning.

She heard nothing but another round of loud knocking. BAM! BAM! BAM!

Mary quickly jumped out of bed, threw a sundress on from the day before, and made her way down the stairs to the front door, combing her hair with her fingers along the way. Before she could reach the door, there was yet another loud BAM, BAM, BAM!

"I'm coming!" she yelled as she approached the door.

She looked through the peephole and saw a man on her doorstep wearing a badge with big letters that read "Sheriff." Her heart was pounding as she opened the door.

"Mary Robinson?" the sheriff barked at her.

"Yes, that's me," she said, hesitantly.

"Is Robert Robinson here?"

"Ahh, I don't think so. Why? What's going on?"

The sheriff handed Mary some papers. "Ma'am, you've been served."

Mary tried reading the legal documents, but the stress of having been awoken by banging at her door had shut down her ability to think clearly. "What is this?" she asked anxiously.

"It's an eviction notice, ma'am. I'm sorry to deliver the bad news."

"What does it mean?" she asked.

"It means you have fourteen days to remove all your stuff and be out of here before the landlord comes back with a police officer and a moving company to move it all into storage at your expense."

"Fourteen days, really?"

He responded more softly this time. "It's serious, ma'am. You're going to need to find a new place to live." He turned around and walked back to his car.

Mary just stood there, hair disheveled, documents in hand, mouth wide open. She was in shock. *Where the heck is Robby?* she wondered. *This is a frigging nightmare.*

Mary closed the door and called Robby on his cellphone, but there was no answer. "Call me right away. Where are you? Robby, I need you to come home now. Something terrible has happened."

She walked into the kitchen and saw a note propped on the counter. She picked it up and it read: *Left early this morning, sweetie. Lots to do. Didn't want to wake you. I'll call you later. Love, Robby.*

Mary shuffled into the living room and sat down on the sofa, stunned. *How are we going to afford to move? We don't have any money for food; how are we going to have enough money for a new apartment?*

She curled up on the sofa and began to cry. She remained there waiting for her husband to call her back, the husband who had told her to take her time finding a new job, that she didn't need to worry about the rent while she was looking. Well, now she was worried.

CHAPTER SIX:

THE RESURRECTION

DAVE ROBINSON was sitting up in bed with his legs crossed and his hands turned palms up resting on his knees when Nurse Paula burst into the room and flicked the fluorescent lights on. "Good morning, Dave!" she said in her famously loud voice.

Dave's eyes popped open, and his whole body jumped. "Geez, Paula! Are you trying to give me a heart attack?"

She grabbed his arm and began checking his blood pressure. She was a hefty, hard woman with a strong grip. Nothing was gentle about Paula except her heart. She was the kindest, most compassionate nurse in the hospital, only with a rough bedside manner.

"I won't give you a heart attack, Dave. It's not your heart that's the problem. What's this? You're meditating now?"

"Well, I was trying. It's kind of hard with nurses and technicians flying in here every five minutes to poke and prod me. You know, there's a lot of evidence that meditation is good for one's health."

"I know," said Paula. "I've read the medical journals. You don't need to convince me. I'm just wondering, why the sudden interest?" She finished taking his blood pressure, rolled the blood pressure machine aside, and put her stethoscope to his chest.

Dave waited until she removed the earpieces of the stethoscope to answer her. "My son visited me. He reminded me of something I once knew but sadly had forgotten. And forgetting is the reason I got sick."

She gave him a frown. "It wasn't the cigarettes that made you sick?"

"The cigarettes were *how* I got sick, not *why* I got sick. I allowed myself to get sick because I had forgotten why I needed to be healthy."

"Okay, now you're getting philosophical on me," she teased. "They warned me about you. Time for me to leave." She headed for the door.

"Wait, Paula! I'm serious about this. This room isn't going to work. I need a place I can meditate quietly. Any ideas?"

Without hesitation, Paula said, "The chapel. You should go to the chapel. That's where I go when I need a few minutes of peace. It's nice and quiet there. Nobody bothers you."

"Yeah, but I'm not religious."

She snickered. "Neither am I! That doesn't matter. Everyone is welcome in the chapel."

"But I can't get there on my own."

"Again, not a problem," responded Paula. "The hospital chaplain will be happy to roll you back and forth. He's got a lot of extra time on his hands," she added. "I'll tell you what. I'll set it up for you."

"Really?" asked Dave.

"Really," said Paula with a smirk. "To make up for almost giving you a heart attack." Then she hustled out the door.

Dave got back into position to start meditating again. A minute later, Betsy swung open the door with a tray full of food. "Breakfast!"

Dave sighed and pulled the blankets over himself. *Maybe tomorrow*, he thought. *Tomorrow's a new day.*

CHAPTER SEVEN:
THE PAST

ROBBY ENTERED his father's house, and it was like walking back in time. Little had changed in six years. It held the same sofa, same TV, same dining room table and chairs, and same refrigerator. Even the carpets and artwork were the same. A thousand memories of his childhood rushed over him.

Robby saw a family photo on a table and picked it up. Tears sprang to his eyes, and he fell to his knees in grief. It was a photo of his mom, dad, and himself taken just before the accident that killed his mother. He kneeled on the carpet, holding the frame to his chest. His entire body convulsed as he surrendered to the grief.

If he had only gone shopping with her, maybe things would have turned out differently. Instead he told his mother he was busy, but what he'd really done was read a magazine. Maybe she would still be alive if he had gone. He could have warned her. Instead, a truck driver nodded off and drove his eighteen-wheeler across the median strip on the highway. His mother never saw it coming. She never made it to the store, and she never came home again.

Robby cried, sitting on the living room carpet, until his cellphone rang. He looked and saw it was Mary. He wasn't ready to answer it. He wanted to gather himself together first. He put the family photo down on a table, walked into the kitchen, and from there went down the basement stairs and into his father's office.

He flicked the lights on and looked around. Again, it was as if time had frozen the past in place. His dad hadn't changed one single thing in the house. Even his mother's magazines were still on the coffee table. *It's no wonder he's sick*, thought Robby. *He's living in a constant state of grief.*

He saw a photo of his dad getting the key to the city for humanitarian work he had done improving city shelters. Another picture showed his mom at her art opening. Then there were photos of Robby in his Cub Scout uniform, playing the lead in the high school play, and him and Mary before going to a prom.

"It's been six years, for crying out loud. Stop living in the past, Dad," he said out loud, knowing no one could hear him.

Robby spotted the picture of himself next to Wayne Gretzky, holding the signed puck. It was on the wall in front of his father's desk, right where it had always been. He snatched the photo off the wall and then shut the lights off before rushing up the stairs. His heart ached from just being in the house. There were never-ending reminders of his mom around every corner. He watered the plants using the blender pitcher from the kitchen, locked the front door, hopped in his pickup truck, and drove away toward Matt's sports memorabilia store.

Fifteen minutes later, Matt saw him outside the store through the window. Robby was walking toward the store from the parking lot with the puck and framed photograph in his hands. Because the store was filled with customers, Matt quickly filled out some paperwork and grabbed some cash from the register. When Robby entered the store, Matt showed him where to sign and gave him the cash.

"As you can see, I'm a little busy," said Matt. He patted Robby on the back and added, "Nice doing business with you, Poopstain. I still think you're crazy letting go of this, but somebody is going to be a happy customer."

"Thanks, Matt. Let's not spend so much time together next time."

Matt nodded with a smile. "I'm sorry. Duty calls. Not everybody gets to sit around and write stories all day long," he teased.

Robby waved him off and counted out the three hundred and fifty dollars before he stuffed the bills in his pocket. He took one last look at the hockey puck and photo to burn the experience into his memory. On the one hand, he was happy to have some money for food. On the other hand, he felt sick for selling one of his favorite childhood memories for a little cash. *How did my life get here*? he wondered.

Matt was already talking to customers, so Robby quietly slipped outside. He checked his cellphone in the parking lot. Mary had called again, so he called her back without listening to her message. He had dozens of voicemail messages that he had never played because he customarily returned calls without listening. There was no answer on Mary's phone. *I'll try again in a few minutes*, he decided. *She's probably just wondering where I am.*

Taking a short detour on the drive home to Boylston, Robby drove to one his favorite spots by the Wachusett Reservoir in Oakdale. He pulled over where the Quinapoxet River met the reservoir and there was a fifteen-foot waterfall just a short walk up the river. Robby often sat on the rocks there and soaked in the sun when he had something important to contemplate. He figured it would be a great place to do his mala exercise for the first time.

He grabbed the mala beads and booklet and walked over to the rocks. He looked around to be sure he was alone. Then he held his mala in one hand and read the Sanskrit abundance mantra aloud, referring to the booklet, as he fingered each mala bead. "Om shrim maha Lakshmiyei swaha. Om shrim maha Lakshmiyei swaha. Om shrim maha Lakshmiyei swaha . . . "

As he spoke each word, he thought about the significance of thanking the goddess of abundance with deep respect for all the abundance he was receiving from her. He immediately felt the power of the ritual. Within no time he had memorized the mantra and didn't have to read it from the manual. By the time he had repeated the mantra for the 108th time, Robby felt empowered and hopeful for a better future.

When he was done, he lay down on the rock and bathed in the serenity that had overcome him. With eyes closed, he listened to the sound of the waterfall and breeze. He could smell the grass and wildflowers surrounding him. His entire body and mind were buzzing with positive energy. The sun's rays had made the rock warm, and within minutes he fell into a deep sleep.

CHAPTER EIGHT:

THE DESPERATION

MARY COULDN'T wait for Robby any longer. She knew what needed to be done. She went to the top drawer of her dresser and grabbed her mother's antique ring. It was time. She had to sell it.

She felt sure that if she took the money to the landlord he'd stop the eviction proceedings, even if she and Robby were a few hundred short. She always saw people in their best light, so she believed the landlord would show them compassion. She straightened her sundress, combed her hair, and put her cellphone in her purse.

When she arrived at Jankowitz Jewelers, Mary wasn't even thinking about losing the only belonging of her mother's she had. She was focused on getting the money she and Robby needed so they wouldn't be evicted. She was determined and doing what she had to do to survive.

As she walked from her car to the building, her cellphone rang. She looked at the caller ID and saw it was Robby. *Great timing, Robby,* she thought. She knew she couldn't answer because he'd ask where she was, and if she told him, he'd try to stop her from selling the ring. He would never allow it without an argument, but she knew it was the only way. She put her phone on vibrate and tossed it back into her purse.

When she entered the jewelry store, there was a twenty-something woman behind the counter. There was no sign of Eva. Before the young clerk had an opportunity to greet her, Mary started talking without saying hello. "I need to see the owner, please. He'll know what this is about."

"And your name?" asked the girl politely as she grabbed a paper and pen from behind the counter.

"Mary Robinson. I don't think he knows my last name. I was here two days ago. He's interested in buying my mother's ring."

"Well, Mr. Jankowitz isn't in today."

"Is Eva here?"

"I'm sorry, she's not here either."

"Then can you call him? I'm sure he'll come in if you explain to him what this is about."

"I'm sorry, Mary. He specifically told me not to call him today. He's dealing with a family emergency."

Mary's stiff, determined body was ready to overcome whatever obstacle the girl put in front of her, but when she heard "family emergency," it brought back personal memories of her parents' illnesses. Both had been sick for a couple of years before they died, which had been hard on Mary. Her determination slowly deflated. She took a deep breath, hoping to make one more attempt.

"Is there anyone else here who has the authority to buy my ring?"

"I'm sorry. Mr. Jankowitz is the only one. But if you leave your number, he can call you when he returns."

Mary wrote her cellphone number down on the piece of paper the clerk gave her and asked, "Will that be later today?"

"To be honest, I believe he'll be out for a few days. I really am very sorry. I'll make sure he calls you when he returns."

Mary's head became cloudy. Her plan was derailed. All she could do was mumble a thank you and walk out the door. She got back in her car and tried to think. Her whole body felt numb. She called her friend Caroline, who answered right away.

"Mary! It's so nice to hear from you."

"Caroline," she said softly, "can I come see you? I need to talk."

"I'm not home, Mary. But I can meet you at Pinecroft Dairy in West Boylston in half an hour. Does that work for you?"

"That works. I'll see you there. Thanks."

CHAPTER NINE:

THE DREAM

ASLEEP ON THE rock by the waterfall near the reservoir, Robby dreamed that he was holding his mala and sitting beside his mother.

"Mom, it's so good to see you," Robby said in his dream.

"It's good to see you too, son." She lifted his hand from the rock and held it. His entire body was overcome with her love.

"You look great, Mom. Younger."

"I'm in a wonderful place, Robby—our true home. I'm here to tell you that everything is going to be all right. I helped you find that in the attic." She motioned toward the mala.

"Really? You helped me find this? Is it really magical?"

"The mala will teach you what most people forget when they are born."

"What's that?"

"For starters, that everyone is connected to the Ultimate Power that created all there is."

"God?"

"Yes, God. Everyone and everything is connected to God and to one another. And every person has the same creative power that God has. It all begins with your thoughts, words, and actions. This is what the mala will teach you. Pay attention, son. You have much to learn. Now I have to go."

"Oh please don't go, Mom!" But she was already gone.

A noisy crow flew over Robby sleeping on the rock, and its squawking woke him up. He opened his eyes but had to squint due to the bright sunlight. He saw the crow land on a tree branch nearby and heard it caw.

Robby sat on the rock thinking about the dream. *Was it real? It sure felt real. It was a dream, but it didn't feel like any other dream. It felt like a visit from Mom . . . a visit from heaven.*

Robby looked at his watch to see that it was late afternoon. *Oh no, Mary's going to be worried.* He got up to go buy some groceries with his hockey puck money and then get home to Mary. *She'll be happy that we have some food to eat,* he thought. *No more boxed macaroni and cheese for a while.*

CHAPTER TEN:

THE OPEN DOOR

MARY WAS ONLY ten minutes from the restaurant and ice cream parlor, which was just enough time to give her an opportunity to collect herself. When she arrived, Caroline was waiting in the parking lot. They hugged, but Mary cut the hug short because she didn't want to get emotional again. The ladies walked inside and got seated at a table.

Mary immediately told Caroline her whole story, revealing the secrets she and Robby had been keeping from people about their financial struggles.

"You know, Mary, it must have been divine intervention that the jewelry store owner wasn't there today," Caroline said. "You can't sell your mother's ring. It was a blessing in your favor."

That wasn't what Mary had expected her friend to say. She had thought Caroline would encourage her to try another jewelry store or wait until the following week.

Mary had always respected Caroline's advice ever since they were schoolmates. In high school, Caroline was the head cheerleader. But unlike many of the snobby cheerleaders on her squad, she had a heart of gold. Caroline had been friends with everyone, regardless of their social status in school. Because of it, everyone liked her.

Mary always thought it was odd that she and Caroline were best friends given how introverted and much less socially outgoing she was than her friend. Mary preferred to be painting or drawing rather than going to a party. Yet for some reason, on some important level, the two girls had clicked. Now they'd been friends for more than fifteen years.

"I know you're right," Mary replied. "It probably was divine intervention. But we're being evicted and selling that ring is the only solution I could think of right now. If I can go to the landlord with that money, I'm sure I can talk him out of the eviction."

Caroline looked at Mary endearingly. "Sweetie, if you were served eviction papers, he's not going to change his mind. He's already got a court-ordered eviction. I know you like to see the best in people, but to him it's just a business transaction. You haven't paid your rent, so he has to get you out of there. You're a business risk even if you pay him what you owe him."

A petite waitress arrived to take their orders. She seemed too young to be out of school at this time of the day. Even her voice was soft and squeaky like a child's. "Welcome to Pinecroft Dairy and Restaurant. How can I help you ladies?" she said. "Are you here for lunch?"

"I think I'm just going to get a hot fudge sundae," said Mary.

"Ooh, that sounds good to me, too," said Caroline.

The waitress left and Caroline held Mary's hand in hers from across the table. "Even though you can't see another solution right now, the Universe is always supporting you. Say that out loud, Mary."

"The Universe is always supporting me."

"It's possible that there's a better apartment out there waiting for you. I'm sure you've heard that when one door closes another one opens. This means that change can be good. Sometimes we can't see it when we're in the middle of it, but that's what faith is all about. You and Robby never really liked your apartment anyway, right?"

Mary laughed softly. Her demeanor softened. "No, we never really did."

"So why all the resistance to being evicted? Is it really that bad?"

"Well, yes, because we don't have any place to go and we don't have any money to pay for the first month, last month, and security deposit that most landlords require."

"I can teach you how to deal with that. I really wish you had come to one of my recent manifestation workshops. It doesn't matter, though. I can teach you what you need to know privately."

"I don't know if that's a good idea. You know how Robby feels about that stuff. Frankly, he can be a pain in the neck about anything that can't be proven, and I don't feel like listening to his skepticism about it. I've learned to just avoid the aggravation."

"But you can prove it. Take Matt, for example. He used to be that way, too, before we got married. However, when he opened his first store and nobody was coming in, he opened his mind to the practice of setting intentions because he had to pay the bills. And you've seen what it's done for him. He now has three stores that are all thriving. He uses the same principles I teach my students every day. He's proven to himself that it works."

Mary's eyes widened. "We certainly could use a little help in our lives right now."

"It's not black magic I'm teaching, Mary. I simply show people how to set intentions and use their thoughts to create whatever they want in their lives. You're right. This is *exactly* what you need right now."

"I guess if Robby chooses not to believe in such things, he doesn't have to know about it if you teach me. I've never kept secrets from him before, but if you think this can help us the way it helped Matt, then I can live with one secret until we get through this crisis."

Caroline pulled out a pen from her purse and turned Mary's paper placemat over. "Let me show you how easy it is. Write this down: 'When one door closes, another one opens to something better. A better apartment is waiting for us.'"

Mary wrote it down.

"Okay, good," said Caroline. "Now repeat that phrase to yourself every time you have a negative thought about being evicted."

Mary said it out loud. "When one door closes, another one opens to something better. A better apartment is waiting for me and Robby."

The waitress delivered the hot fudge sundaes and asked if there was anything else she could get for them.

"I'd like a new apartment with that," Mary said jokingly.

Caroline laughed, happy to see her friend feeling lighter.

The waitress said, "You know, there's a bulletin board over there and one of our regular customers came in this morning with a notice for an apartment. It might be worth a look. She's a real nice lady, and a good tipper."

The waitress got called over by the manager, and Caroline scooted out of the booth. She ran over to the bulletin board and came back with the ad. "It says it's a five-year-old condominium with a view of the reservoir." She looked up at Mary. "Sounds sweet." She looked back at the paper. "All utilities included, only nine hundred and fifty dollars a month!"

Mary didn't seem excited. "Sounds great, but that's more than we pay now—well, maybe not, since it includes utilities." She took out a pen and did some math quickly on her placemat. "But that would mean we'd need to come up with about two thousand eight hundred and fifty dollars. If I had that, I wouldn't be in this mess right now."

"Okay, there's one of those negative and limiting thoughts. Read that affirmation three times to offset it."

Mary did what Caroline suggested. She trusted her friend. She thought about how Caroline had helped Matt turn the sports memorabilia store around. They'd since bought a house, both were driving new cars, and they had money saved for retirement.

"What do you say we call that lady and go see the condo?" suggested Caroline.

"What? No . . . seriously?" Mary giggled at the thought of it.

"What harm can it do? Get out your phone and call right now. It's a good practice. How can you visualize what it would be like to live there if you don't see it?"

Mary called the number, and the lady answered immediately. She was very friendly, and, to Mary's surprise, the woman asked if she wanted to see the condo at five o'clock, which was only an hour away. Mary agreed, and she and Caroline were on their way after finishing their ice cream sundaes.

As the two women got in Caroline's car, Mary's cellphone rang. It was Robby. She answered the call and told him she was with Caroline. He sounded so happy that she decided to wait to tell him in person about the eviction notice. *There will be plenty of time for that later*, she thought. *Plus, I finally feel hopeful, and I don't want to ruin it.*

Mary told Robby she loved him and that he'd probably need to eat supper on his own. She'd be late getting home. After hanging up, she was feeling deeply grateful for her friend Caroline, and she told her so on the drive over to see the condo.

CHAPTER ELEVEN:

THE HELPING HAND

DAVE SAT UP in his hospital bed, amazed at how different he felt from two mornings prior when he'd woken up waiting to die. Today he woke up eager to live. He had dreamed of his wife during the night, and she helped him to remember that his life was a precious gift.

"It's the most valuable gift anyone can give," Margie had told him in the dream. "A gift given to you by someone who loves you more than you'll ever know."

Dave now recognized that he had been squandering his life because he was unable to accept Margie's death.

He said to his wife silently in his thoughts, *I understand now that I can't stop living my life because your life stopped six years ago. It's not what you want for me, I know. I see more clearly than ever now that with the gift of life comes joy and pain, love and heartbreak, success and failure. It is our free will that allows us to choose what we focus upon. I promise, honey, that I will now focus on the love that is all around me, and the love you and I shared, rather than the pain I feel from losing you.*

Dave could still feel his wife's presence. He knew she had really visited him in his dream because he could still feel her near him now that he was awake. He remained as still as possible, hoping not to lose the connection.

The door to Dave's room opened after a quiet knock. "May I come in?" asked a gentle voice.

"Come in," answered Dave.

The hospital chaplain entered Dave's room wearing black pants and a black shirt with a white clerical collar. He was a small, wiry man in his mid-sixties with a kind, pleasant manner. "Hello, Mr. Robinson. I'm Jonathan Burke," he said casually, as he walked toward Dave's bed to shake his hand.

"Father Burke, nice to meet you. Please call me Dave." Then he paused, unsure. "Do I call you *Father*? Are you Catholic?"

"Episcopalian. But I think of myself as offering multi-faith spiritual guidance now that I work here in the hospital. Still, you got it right: Father Burke is correct, if you want to be formal about it. Jonathan is fine, too."

"Well, I appreciate you coming, Father," Dave said, wanting to be respectful.

"Not at all. Paula told me you're looking for a place to meditate and that she suggested the chapel."

"Yes, is that permitted?"

"Of course it is. That's what most people do there. We just have another name for it; we call it praying." Father Burke's bright blue eyes lit up, knowing he was being clever.

Dave smiled and nodded. "I never thought of it like that, but you're right. Meditation and prayer have a lot in common."

The minister sat on the end of Dave's bed. "I sit in daily silence myself," he said. "I've been doing it for so long now that it takes me no time at all before my mind goes blank and my fingers and hands get tingly. Before I know it, forty-five minutes have gone by and my entire body feels like it's floating in the air. When my awareness comes back to the room, I feel twenty years younger. My mind is more alert, and my body is filled with energy. Is that your experience with meditation?"

Dave was nearly speechless. "Ahh yes, definitely, that's exactly my experience. At least it used to be. I haven't done it for a long time. I gave it up about six years ago."

Father Burke leaned in. "And why is that, may I ask?"

Dave took a deep breath. "Everything between us is confidential, right? Even if I'm not of your religion?"

"I don't discriminate in confidentiality," Father Burke said with a smile. "I'm merely here to serve."

"Well, I stopped doing everything I believed in after my wife died. She was forty-nine years old, and I had just turned fifty-four. To be honest, I lost my desire to live. I spent most of my days wishing I could join her. I stopped working, stopped golfing, stopped meditating, and pretty much stopped living. And that made me feel guilty because I have a son who was twenty-six when his mother died. He's thirty-two now."

"And how did life turn out for you after that?" asked the minister.

"You're looking at it. Within a year of my wife's death I got lung cancer, which left me with only half a lung. And, for the last four years, I've spent way too much time getting to know the doctors and nurses around here."

Father Burke waited to be sure Dave was done talking, then asked, "And now, my friend? What do you want now? Why the desire to begin meditating again?"

"Well that's the question, isn't it?" said Dave. He looked out the window at the clouds. "If I'm being honest, it's because my son needs me. I didn't think he did. Quite frankly, I didn't think I had anything to offer him, mostly because he never wanted to hear what I had to say after he graduated from college. But he came in here the other day eager to hear my thoughts. It made me realize I have a lot to give him . . . well, *teach* him is probably the better word. And I know his mother would want that."

Dave sat up straight in the bed and put his hand on Father Burke's knee. "I don't know if you believe in this sort of thing or not, but my wife came to me in a dream last night. She asked me to turn my life around to help our son. And in the dream, I promised her I would. Even awake, I really would like to honor that promise if I can."

"I've seen too much not to believe in such things, Dave. So do you think you can do what you promised?"

"I think I can share what I know with him about being success-ful in life and business. What he does with my advice is up to him. But I think he came in here the other day simply needing his dad. I know I'm not much good to him in this place, and certainly not if I'm dead, so I want to turn my health around and see if I can make up for the last six years. I realize now how selfish and self-destruc-tive I've been. I'm not proud of it, but it's not too late to change. Does that make sense, Father?"

It all sounded familiar to the minister. The story of what happened to Dave and his son, Robby, reminded him of his own childhood. His mother had died giving birth to him, after which his father left him with his mother's parents. His grandparents were wonderful parents to young Jonathan, but he had always longed for a relationship with his biological father. Unfortunately, he was never able to meet him.

He later learned that his father had drunk himself into isolation and homelessness.

"It makes more sense to me than you'll ever know," he told Dave. "So I'd like to help you in any way that I can. How about I pick you up here every morning at seven and every afternoon at four? I'll bring you back and forth to the chapel until they kick you out of here for being too healthy. Is that a good start?"

"Come here, Father," said Dave, as he leaned over to hug him. "We'll begin tomorrow?"

"Tomorrow it is," answered Father Burke before he left. He closed the door on his way out so that Dave could have a moment to sit with what he had just acknowledged to the minister.

CHAPTER TWELVE:

THE INSPIRATION

CAROLINE AND MARY walked up to the condo that was available for rent with Jenny, the woman who owned it, leading the way. Jenny was in her mid-sixties, a high school teacher who was new to retirement. And she was clearly proud of the space she was showing them.

The three women chatted while Jenny showed them the spacious yard, being that the condo was an end unit. Mary noticed the flower beds all around it. "The flowers are fabulous. This seems to be the only condo that has them. Did you plant them?" she asked Jenny.

"Thank you for noticing. Yes, I did it myself. I was a little more limber five years ago. I'm so glad I did it. They really add some beauty, don't they? These are tulips that bloom in early spring. Over here are irises and peonies that come out in late spring. These are Shasta daisies and over here are hydrangeas, which both bloom in summer. Finally, over here are my sunflowers that stick around into the fall."

"You put so much thought into it," said Mary. "I love painting flowers. I'd have something new to paint every season, and right in my own yard."

Jenny's face brightened. "Oh my goodness, what a nice idea. Would you consider teaching me? I would pay you. I've always wanted to learn to paint."

"I've never taught before, but that would be fun—sure!"

Jenny asked some questions about Mary and Robby. She learned that Robby was a writer and Mary was between jobs. She learned that they'd been together for about fifteen years and married for five. In return, Mary learned that Jenny and her husband were both recently retired and lived only a few miles away.

"We bought this place for my father five years ago, just after it was built. He passed sooner than we expected. It's been empty for over a year because I wasn't ready to rent it yet. I don't know why, but this morning I just knew it was time."

"I'm sorry for your loss," said Mary. "As young as I am, I've already lost both my parents and I know how difficult it can be."

Jenny touched Mary's arm with a smile and nodded, then led them up the front stairs. As they entered the front door, sunlight was pouring through the large windows in the front of the condominium. The living room and kitchen were one big sundrenched space. The living room had a cathedral ceiling that reflected the light, making the place appear larger than its actual size.

Mary and Caroline were first drawn toward a picture window that overlooked the sparkling water of the reservoir. "The sunsets are gorgeous here," boasted Jenny. "It sometimes makes the whole place turn red and orange. Of course, all this furniture will be taken out of here to empty it for the new tenants. If you like any of it, I'll give you a good deal."

As Caroline and Mary walked into the large galley kitchen, Caroline whispered to her friend while Jenny was closing the front door, "Did you pick up on that? She knew it was time to rent just this morning after waiting for a year. Do you think it's just a fluke that you happened to get an eviction notice on the same morning? I don't think so. This condo has been waiting for you."

It was all very dreamy to Mary, but she couldn't help wondering still how she and Robby were possibly going to get the money required for the lease.

Jenny walked into the kitchen. "I should have mentioned that, because it's a condo, all the yard work is done for you by the condo association. The lawn is mowed and raked. The hedges are trimmed. They even take care of the snow in the winter."

"What about the flower beds? I love planting and weeding," said Mary. "I find it relaxing."

"No, the condo association doesn't do that. I've been doing it myself, but to be honest I don't love it as much as I once did. It hurts my back too much. If that's something you enjoy, you would be welcome to do it."

Jenny showed the girls the half bathroom and the office downstairs and the bedroom with the master bathroom upstairs. There wasn't a room in the place that wasn't glimmering with light. Big windows were everywhere. There was even a one-car garage.

The three women chatted for about an hour after the tour. They laughed and told stories. Mary and Jenny talked about the difficulties of losing a parent. When it was time to go, Jenny handed Mary some papers.

"This is the lease. I would love to rent the condo to you and your husband. We'll be showing it to other people, but I can't imagine we'll find anyone as nice as you. Take the weekend and think about it. Talk it over with your husband, and give me a call if he's interested in seeing it. Okay?"

Mary agreed and thanked Jenny. As she and Caroline left, they both stopped to look out the picture window again at the sun that was now setting low in the sky over the reservoir. It all seemed surreal to Mary, so much that she didn't want to go home and spoil her mood by breaking the eviction news to Robby.

On their way back to Pinecroft Dairy, where they had left Mary's car, the women fantasized about how inspiring it would be for Mary and Robby to live in the condo. They agreed to talk the next morning. Caroline reminded Mary of everything they'd discussed about intentions while eating their hot fudge sundaes and made Mary promise that she'd repeat her affirmation every time her thoughts became fearful or pessimistic.

CHAPTER THIRTEEN:
THE UNFORESEEABLE

MARY CALLED CAROLINE on the phone the morning after looking at Jenny's condo. "Do you really believe I found that apartment because I read that affirmation? Wasn't that kind of fast for it to be anything more than coincidence?"

"Mary, time doesn't exist metaphysically. Everything is happening at once. Plus, you didn't just say the affirmation; you also took action when you asked that waitress for an apartment with the sundaes."

"Yeah, but I was joking."

"The Universe doesn't understand the difference between what we say that is serious and what we say that is humorous. It also doesn't know the difference between positive and negative. You went from the thought of finding an apartment, to actually writing 'a better apartment is waiting for me and Robby,' to then saying it out loud. By doing so, you took three steps that sent a powerful message to the Universe that you want a better apartment. And because you were so emotional at the time, that gave the affirmation more power. When we add feelings to our intentions, it's like adding fuel to a fire. It increases the potency of an intention exponentially."

"I certainly was emotional considering all the drama yesterday," Mary admitted.

"When you then asked the waitress for an apartment with your hot fudge sundae, you were taking action in a joyful way to manifest the outcome you desired. Taking action not only sends a powerful message to the Universe, it also assists the Universe in delivering your request to you. If your action is in alignment with your thoughts and words, it's a 'triple threat.'"

"I don't entirely understand about the action part," confessed Mary.

Caroline, a natural-born teacher, loved sharing her intention practices. She jumped to her feet with enthusiasm and paced as she talked on the phone. "The thought of wanting a better apartment was your intention. Saying your affirmation out loud multiple times is called attention. It's the act of giving your intention attention, otherwise known as *focus*. In your case, what you focused upon created a stronger attraction. Asking the waitress for a better apartment helped the Universe connect you with the notice on the bulletin board. That, too, was attention in the form of action—you asked a stranger for a new apartment.

"You see, Mary, if all we do is set an intention and then sit on the sofa waiting for positive results to come into our lives, it's more challenging for the Universe to send us what we desire. But if we take action aligned with an intention, we help the Universe bring the intention into reality. We become like a pinball in a pinball machine that is bouncing around bumping into people that the Universe might be able to use to help us. Does that make sense?"

"I think I understand. Because time doesn't exist in the spiritual dimension, the Universe somehow already knew I was going to be evicted before I knew it. Consequently, it might have been working for a while to set up a new apartment for me to see that morning, which is why Jenny decided to rent the condo on that very day. Is that right?"

"Exactly. What's important about what you just said, Mary, is that everything we want from life is already available to us. The Universe has already made it so. Our job is to 'claim it,' which is another way of saying we must 'allow it' to come into our lives. Once you embrace this concept, creating the life of your desires will become effortless for you."

"Okay, so I just need to claim or allow it. And if that's the case, then Jenny might have been guided to post the apartment on the bulletin board at Pinecroft Dairy because the Universe knew I would be meeting you there. But it's possible that I might not have seen or found out about the bulletin board notice at all if I hadn't joked with the waitress. So my action—the joke I spontaneously made—helped the Universe help me."

"That's it!" yelled Caroline over the phone in her excitement.

Matt heard his wife yell and yelled back, "Are you calling me?"

"No, honey, I'm on the phone with Mary."

"Oh good. Have her tell Skidmark that his hockey puck went to a good home."

Caroline relayed the message to Mary.

Mary was familiar with the puck. She had asked Robby about the photo of him and Gretzky the first time she saw it on Dave's office wall. Since then, Robby had mentioned this special childhood memento many times over the years. "I don't understand," said Mary. "Does that mean Robby sold his hockey puck for money?"

"I think so, sweetie."

"You know what, Caroline? Robby was asleep last night when I got home, so we haven't talked yet. I've been anxious about telling him about the eviction notice, and I don't even know how I'm going to bring up the subject of Jenny's condo for rent. But I can hear he's awake now and moving around downstairs, so I guess I need to go talk with him. It was nice chatting with you. Thanks for the private lesson."

"No problem, Mary. Good luck."

Robby was downstairs in his office writing in his journal. He had just finished his mala practice and already had much to record. He wrote:

DAY 3, Morning

I've memorized the mantra without looking at the booklet, and I'm pretty sure that I understand the meaning behind all the words. I'm also watching my thoughts and words to keep them positive. I never realized how often my thoughts go to negativity. Every time I think or express my worries and fears, I am doing my best to remember to offset that with an affirmation that is positive. If I've noticed anything it's that I definitely feel happier and more at peace now, even if nothing concrete has occurred yet in terms of abundance. Still, I'm hopeful that it's on its way.

Just as he was about to write a description of the dream in which his mother visited him by the waterfall, Mary walked into his office. She'd brought him a cup of his favorite drink, a personal invention he called *cofftea,* which was three quarters of a cup of licorice and mint tea mixed with one quarter of a cup of black coffee.

"It's good to see you writing again," she said, placing his cofftea on his desk. "Also, here's today's mail. The top one says S. Thurston. Isn't that your last client?" She handed Robby the small stack of mail she had tucked under her arm.

"Yeah, Samuel. I wonder why he wrote me. He usually emails." Robby sorted through the envelopes. Almost all were bills, most of them now pink slips. He opened the envelope from Samuel. "What the—?" Enclosed with Samuel's letter was a check for five thousand dollars. Robby's heart began to pound as he handed the check to Mary. He was dumbfounded and skeptical.

"Don't get excited yet," he told her. "This must be some kind of mistake." Robby unfolded the letter and read it aloud. "Because of your brilliant writing, I just got an advance on the book you ghost-wrote for me from Irving and Kittredge Publishing. They absolutely love it! To express my appreciation, I'm sending you a bonus. I'll give you the details next time I'm in town."

"Wow, honey," exclaimed Mary, "that's amazing! Congratulations." She was jumping up and down beside Robby in his chair, but he seemed more shocked than happy.

"I can't believe it. No one has ever sent me a bonus before." He read the letter again, suspicious. He examined the check and looked at the envelope. "I guess it's real. The postmark is from his town. My god, this is incredibly generous. No client has ever done anything like this."

Robby's entire demeanor changed from skeptical to enthusiastic. Although he felt a sense of relief that he could now pay the three months' worth of back rent and cover the next month's rent, he knew there wouldn't be much left over after paying the utilities and other bills. As soon as he caught himself viewing the situation from a negative perspective he thought, *I'm not going there. This is a gift, a wonderful gift. The blessing is what I must focus on.*

Robby looked at the check and felt gratitude in his heart, "one of the most powerful frequencies in the Universe," he recalled Tru telling him. He stood up from his desk, put his arms around Mary, and said, "Let's celebrate."

"Can we afford to?"

"Of course we can," he said as he squeezed her body into his. But after thinking about what she said, he added with a smile, "As long as we celebrate with hamburgers."

Mary laughed. "Wonderful. A hamburger for you. A veggie burger for me. It sounds delightful."

The couple went out for one the most enjoyable evenings they'd had in a long time. They ate burgers and cheese fries at Johnny Rockets at the Natick Mall using the hockey puck money Robby had in his pocket. Robby bought Mary a stuffed bear at a kiosk, and they laughed together as they walked around the mall eating hot pretzels and drinking Starbucks coffee.

Robby knew he might feel fearful again tomorrow, but tonight he allowed himself to feel connected to the abundance of the Universe. He had no clue they were being evicted in a matter of days, so to him it felt like their troubles were over. Things were looking up!

All the while she was celebrating Robby's good fortune with him, Mary secretly also celebrated that she wasn't going to have to sell her mother's antique ring anytime soon. She knew she should have told Robby about the sheriff's visit and the eviction notice, but she didn't want to ruin the moment for him. His inability to get a new client these last few months had really lowered his self-confidence, and this bonus from Samuel was the boost Robby needed. She knew it was pressing, too, that she bring up the matter of Jenny's condo, but that could wait as well. They had dodged a bullet, and this was a moment to celebrate.

Tonight there were a lot of reasons to be grateful, and Robby and Mary had both learned within the last forty-eight hours the power of a grateful mind.

CHAPTER FOURTEEN:
THE SALES PITCH

I T HAD BEEN exactly one week since Robby found the mala. Because Samuel's check was from out of state, it needed a few days to clear at the bank before he could spend it. Mary still hadn't told Robby about the eviction notice or the apartment. But it wasn't from fear of upsetting him or procrastination over delivering the bad news. Actually she was trying to be strategic. Although Robby certainly might be upset when he learned they were going to get kicked out in roughly seven days and they hadn't packed a single box, her daddy had always told her to pick her moments carefully when making a sale.

"Everybody is selling something," her daddy said. "Children sell their parents on staying up late. Parents sell their children on eating their vegetables. Employees sell their bosses on giving them a raise. And bosses sell their employees on working hard."

Now Mary felt she needed to sell Robby on how they should best use the bonus money from Samuel. She had allowed him to bask in the joy of Samuel's bonus arriving. Now that the check had cleared, however, she knew she couldn't wait any longer. Robby would be leaving the house to pay the landlord this morning without knowing that the landlord was evicting them. He was in for a shock unless she fessed up and immediately revealed the truth.

It was a beautiful day. The couple had enjoyed a lovely weekend together. Robby had made eggs and French toast for breakfast with the groceries he bought after secretly selling the hockey puck to Matt, which Mary hadn't mentioned yet either to avoid any discussion about it.

Mary finished her breakfast and grabbed Robby by the hand. "I'll clean up since you cooked," she told him, "but first I want to talk with you about something."

Mary led him to the living room sofa. Still holding his hand, she said, "I have some good news and some rather bad news. Please don't say anything until I'm done, okay?" This request was another practice she'd learned from her dad.

Robby agreed to listen before saying anything.

"Well, the rather bad news is that last week while you were out, we were served an eviction notice."

Robby's eyes opened wide. He gasped like he had been sucker punched in the solar plexus. He was about to say something when Mary gently placed two fingers up to his mouth. "Wait! You promised you would wait until I'm done." With great self-restraint, he swallowed his words. His eyes were popping out of his head.

"Because I couldn't get hold of you by phone after the sheriff gave me the notice—and I'll admit that I was very scared and needed you in that moment—I called Caroline, and she met with me. She was the perfect person to help me, so it was actually good that you and I didn't talk about it immediately. We would both have become fearful and panicked, and that wouldn't have allowed either of us to think clearly."

Robby nodded in agreement.

She continued. "Anyway, rather serendipitously Caroline and I discovered an absolutely gorgeous condominium by the reservoir for rent. It's only five years old. It has a view of the water. It has an office downstairs and the bedroom is upstairs, so it's laid out just like this place, but a lot nicer. All the utilities are included. Plus, since it's a condo, all the yard work and snow shoveling is done by the condo association." She paused. "Oh, it also has a one-car garage."

Robby began to talk, but Mary put her fingers up to his lips again. "Not yet, honey," she said. "Jenny, the owner, emailed me before breakfast and said it is ours if we want it. I've already filled out the lease. Once you take a look at the place, if you agree with me, nineteen hundred dollars is all we need to take it."

"Nineteen hundred dollars?" he blurted. "Are you sure that's correct?"

"Yes, the rent is only nine fifty per month, and Jenny said we only need to pay the first month's rent and a security deposit. That would leave us enough to pay all our other overdue bills and get a clean start."

Robby squinted, which Mary knew meant he had concerns.

"I can guess what you're thinking—that we should see if we can stay here. But Jack plans to kick us out no matter what. He hasn't left us any options—not that I blame him as a landlord. Still, I suggest that we use the money we just got to move into this new apartment. Otherwise we're going to pay our back rent and still be broke and have no place to live. We can slowly pay Jack what we owe him, a little at a time, as we earn more money. I suggest we send him ten percent of our income until our debt is paid off."

Robby listened, afraid to say anything.

"Finally, Caroline said that when she and Matt moved into their house, living in a more beautiful environment helped to improve their relationship and their finances because they felt nurtured by where they lived. The new home raised their energy in a way that improved many areas of their life together."

Mary paused and thought for a moment about whether she had anything more to add. Robby still didn't dare say anything. "Okay, that's it. That's all I wanted to say," she concluded.

Robby's face was impossible to read. Now that he could talk, he sat on the sofa in silence. He thought about what he had learned from the mala manual. He thought about all the mornings and afternoons he had practiced with his mala in his office with the door closed, on the rock by the waterfall, and during early morning walks. He wondered if his mala practice was why Samuel had sent the unexpected bonus check. And he considered the possibility that it might have assisted Mary in finding the condo for rent, although the idea didn't make much sense to him.

Robby also knew that what Mary said about the power of improving one's environment was absolutely true. He recalled a study he had read for a psychology class he'd taken in college that proved it.

A city decided to clean up the graffiti, the broken windows in vacant buildings, and the overall ugliness due to neglect and vandalism to see how it might affect the community. To their surprise, not only did the residents keep the city clean, they also began to help clean it up. There was less littering. People began to sweep the sidewalks outside their homes and shops. And what really surprised the project committee was that crime rates, from misdemeanors to felonies, dropped significantly.

Mary awaited Robby's response with her hands clasped in front of her.

"I can't believe you held on to this for so long," he said. "For that, I am sorry. I hate that I wasn't able to help you with this. But I can see you've really thought it through, and everything you've said makes a lot of sense. I can't argue against your reasoning. I'm really proud of you, honey."

"Really?" said Mary.

"Yes, however, I don't feel comfortable paying Jack over time when we have the money now. I already feel too guilty. I know he's evicting us, and I don't blame him for that considering we are three months late. I don't want to make him the enemy when we didn't pay our bills on time. And maybe, just maybe, once we pay him, he might give us a second chance and let us stay."

"Caroline doesn't think so, and neither do I. Plus, I want to move. Wait until you see how gorgeous this condo is!"

"That's not really the point. You know I've taken financial responsibility for our rent, and so I feel responsible for this debt to Jack. I'd like you to support me in doing what I feel is right. I think it's only fair that we don't make Jack wait for his money. Can you understand?"

"I understand that you're an honest man, Robby. I admire that about you. But I don't believe it's a wise financial decision. Also, I never wanted you to feel you have to pay the entire rent when I'm perfectly capable of working and contributing. I'll have a job soon; I'm sure of it. I really wish you would reconsider."

"What's right and what's wise aren't always going to be the same. I have to do what I feel is right or I won't be able to live with my guilty conscience. And I believe that we'll figure out some other way to get into that condo if you're correct about us getting evicted even after I pay Jack."

Robby got off the couch and grabbed his checkbook and truck keys off the coffee table. He kissed Mary on top of her head as he left. She was staring at the floor feeling disappointed. "Let's just see what happens with Jack. It's the right thing to do," he said as he opened the door, still looking at her. She didn't respond, so he walked out.

Mary sat and wondered where she'd gone wrong. She had prepared her case and executed it flawlessly, so she was thrown off balance by Robby's unexpected decision. She did not anticipate that his need to do the right thing would override his sense of logic and reason. Yet, in hindsight, she knew that Robby had always been led by his conscience. She'd always known this about him. So she realized that she shouldn't be overly surprised by it.

Now she was going to have to figure out how to get them into Jenny's condo without her husband's bonus money. That's when her cellphone rang. It was Mr. Jankowitz. He was back at work and still willing to buy her mother's ring.

This is the divine coincidence that Caroline mentioned, she thought after hanging up the phone. *This is my mother's spirit at work, telling me it's okay to sell the ring. There's no way he would have called at this very moment otherwise.*

Mary walked upstairs and got her mother's ring out of her bedroom dresser. She kneeled in front of the picture of her mother that was on the side table next to the bed. She held her mother's ring for possibly the final time, her eyes quickly welling up, and silently prayed to her. *Thank you, Mom, for this final parting gift that has become so significant at this time in my life. If there is one thing I have learned how to do because of your passing, it is survive; and what I have to do with this ring now is exactly that: sell it to guarantee our shelter and provide us with an even better home life than we have known thus far. For this, I am grateful to you.*

Who knew that nearly two decades after you left this world, you would be able to help me and my husband survive an eviction and upgrade to a better home all at the same time? That is how I am choosing to view what I am about to do, and we both know that it will not affect how I feel about you or lessen my connection with you.

Thank you, Mom. I love you.

Reluctantly and with a grieving heart, but with certainty that it was the right thing to do, Mary drove to Jankowitz Jewelers and sold her mother's ring. Mr. Jankowitz lived up to his promise of paying her eighteen hundred in cash for it. The payment was only a hundred short of what she needed to pay Jenny, and there would still be enough in the joint checking account to cover that even with Robby paying all of the back rent to Jack in one lump sum out of his bonus check.

Once Mary left the jewelry store, she called Jenny, who agreed to finalize the lease that day. Mary knew she had to complete the deal before Robby learned how she got the money to pay for it. He would insist on buying back the ring for her otherwise. She also knew Robby was going to love the place, so he would eventually forget what she had sacrificed in order to get there.

"Well, I'm thrilled that you decided to take the place, Mary," said Jenny. "I look forward to meeting your husband." She took Mary's check and handed her a receipt. "We showed it to five other couples over the weekend and all I could think was, *I hope Mary and Robby move in.*"

Mary stood in the kitchen of the condominium that she had just leased. She knew she'd made the right choice. Instead of feeling connected to her mother through the ring, she would feel her mother's presence throughout the condominium.

"Can we move in at any time?" she asked Jenny.

"Yes. We moved my father's furniture out on Saturday, so you don't need to wait until the first of the month. If you can move in on a weekday during business hours, there'll be fewer neighbors around to get in the way of the truck and so forth. Here, I made two sets," Jenny said as she handed Mary the keys.

"Thank you. This is really nice of you," Mary said quietly as she stared out the window overlooking the reservoir.

"Is everything all right, dear? You don't seem as happy as you did the other day," said Jenny.

"No, I'm fine. I'm just thinking about my mother a lot today, but not in a bad way. I'm very happy about moving in here."

Jenny grabbed hold of Mary and gave her a squeeze. "I understand, dear, and I'd like to say one thing. I know that no one can ever replace your mother, but if you ever need an old woman to talk to . . . I'm retired, so I have a lot of extra time for talking. Okay?"

Mary smiled. "That would be lovely. We can talk while I teach you how to paint."

"That's perfect. It's a plan."

Mary left peacefully knowing that Jenny's condo was going to be a good change for her and Robby. When she arrived home, Robby had already returned from paying the landlord. He was watching television and said hello very softly as she entered.

"You're quiet," she said. "Everything go all right with Jack?"

"Yes. He was very surprised to see me. He was a little standoffish at first, but he warmed up once he knew I was there to pay him."

"Okay, so why the glum face?"

"You were right. He still wants us out next week. Doing what's right is its own reward, I guess. I do feel good about that. It's a weight off my shoulders. Only now I have a new one. You think another client will send a bonus check?" he joked.

Mary put her purse on the kitchen counter, grabbed the receipt Jenny gave her, and walked over to sit next to Robby. She handed him the receipt as she sat down.

"What's this?" he said as he read it. "I don't understand. Is this a receipt for the condo you talked about?"

Mary had a big smile on her face as she nodded her headed up and down in excitement.

"How?"

"How doesn't matter. The point is that we're moving into a beautiful condo, and you got to pay Jack what we owe him like you wanted."

Robby sat up straight on the sofa, stared her straight in the eyes, and raised his eyebrows. "But I want to know how."

"Well, you sold your hockey puck to buy groceries, so I sold something of mine to get the condo."

Robby looked at her squinting. "What? Hockey puck? How did you . . . ? Oh right, Caroline! Matt told Caroline, and Caroline told you. But what did you own that was worth this much?"

Mary didn't answer. He thought about what Mary owned that might be worth around nineteen hundred dollars and suddenly it occurred to him. The ring.

"Ohh noo. You didn't. That was the only item you had of your mother's." The news gave Robby's inner critic an opportunity to shame him. *This is my fault. I should have listened to Mary and not paid Jack right away. Why do I always have to do things my way? Look where it's got me. And now Mary sold her ring because of it.*

Mary knew from his face that Robby was beating himself up inside. "I'm okay with it, really. I've given it a lot of thought. Until recently, I hadn't pulled that ring out my dresser for years."

Looking at Mary and her sense of calm and resolve, Robby knew he had to trust her on this one. He pulled Mary close to him and kissed the top of her head. "We can find another way, you know. We can march right back in there and get that ring back. I'll make a deal with him to clean the store for a year or something. He can keep the ring as collateral until I work it off."

Mary sat up straight, one hand on Robby's arm. "No. The way I look at it, my mother helped us get into a new home. How amazing is that? And just wait until you see it. This condo is the beginning of our new life."

Mary stood up, grabbing Robby's hand and pulling him off the sofa. She led him into the hallway and opened a closet door. She reached into the closet, and before pulling out whatever it was that she wanted to show him, she said, "Just so you know that I will never forget my mother's ring . . ." She brought out a canvas upon which she had painted her mother's hands praying, wearing the ring.

Robby stopped breathing for a moment. His eyes became glossy. He put his arm around her shoulders as he stared at the painting. "It's absolutely exquisite."

Mary beamed, her eyes tearing up too.

Robby took Mary's hands and held them in front of him as he looked her in the eyes. "You're amazing, honey. There isn't a day that goes by where you don't surprise me with some remarkable way of looking at life. With all the hardships you've endured, you still manage to find the optimistic perspective rather than acting as a victim. You are the example of the human being I strive to be." He paused. "Thank you, my love. I'm grateful for what you have done."

Robby picked up the painting and brought it into the living room. "So I have only one question for you."

"What's that?" she said.

With a straight face he asked, "How much do you think we can get for it?"

Mary gasped in jest and slapped his shoulder with the back of her hand. "You want to go see the condo?"

"Sure! Let's find the perfect wall for this. It'll be the first item we move there. I think it's only appropriate."

CHAPTER FIFTEEN:

THE ADJUSTMENT

DAVE AND ROBBY sat in the hospital cafeteria eating lunch. The sound of silverware touching plates, glasses clinking in the kitchen, chairs scraping across the floor, and people chattering with one another echoed off the painted concrete block walls. It was the first time the father and son had seen one another since the day they sat in the hospital courtyard talking about the mala beads from the attic.

Robby broke the silence. "Dad, I can't believe they're releasing you today. Three weeks ago you were confined either to a bed or a wheelchair. Now you're dressed and walking around? Geez, you don't even look like the same person."

"It's amazing what the body can do when the mind is focused on health," said Dave.

Father Burke walked into the cafeteria and spotted Dave. He walked behind him and put his hands on Dave's shoulders. Dave looked behind him, smiled, and put his hand over one of Burke's. "Father Burke! Nice to see you."

"Dave, I think it's time you started calling me Jonathan," said the minister.

Dave laughed. "To be honest, I think that ship has sailed, Father . . . you see, there I go again. Besides, I like calling you Father. I respect the life you've chosen. It just feels right . . . if it's okay with you."

"Of course it's okay," said Burke. "It really doesn't matter to me what you call me. I just didn't want you to feel it's necessary, especially now that we're friends."

Dave looked at Robby. "Son, I want you to meet a good friend of mine. This is Father Burke. Father, this is my son, Robby."

Robby stood to shake Father Burke's hand. He'd never known his father to be religious, so he couldn't imagine how he knew this man wearing a white collar.

"Nice to meet you, Robby. Your father has told me a lot of nice things about you. I hear you're a writer."

"Nice to meet you, too. How do you know . . ."

"The father here writes as well," Dave interrupted. "He writes beautiful poetry."

Burke waved off the compliment. "I'm an amateur. Look, I don't want to interrupt. Just wanted to say hello. I'm going to miss this guy," he said to Robby, patting Dave on the shoulder.

"I'll see you next Thursday," Dave reminded him. Turning to Robby, he said, "I'm taking Father Burke to Mechanics Hall for the Gregorian chant concert."

"That ought to be fun. Not my thing, but it's right up your alley, Dad."

"Mine as well," said the minister. "I'm looking forward to it."

They said their goodbyes and Father Burke went up to the food line.

"You told me you weren't religious, Dad. What am I missing here?"

"The father helped me out while I was here. We became friends. It's the oldest religion, son: friendship. If it weren't for him, I might not be leaving this quickly. He's a good man."

Robby was silent. He picked up his tuna fish sandwich and wiped a glob of ketchup off the plate with it.

Dave grimaced. "I can't believe you still put ketchup on your tuna fish. Who does that? Did Mom teach you that, because I certainly didn't?"

His father's comment triggered the memory of Robby's dream where his mother visited him. He was tempted to tell his dad about it but felt certain his dad wouldn't believe it was real. The dream was sacred and comforting to Robby, so he didn't want his dad to ruin it for him. He decided not to mention it.

"How are things going with you?" asked Dave, interrupting Robby's thoughts. "Are you still using the mala?"

"I sure am." Robby pulled the mala out of his pocket and held it in the air to prove he had it with him. "Twice a day and on any other opportunity I can find. I'm on day twenty-two of my forty-day commitment."

"That's great. Have you seen any results?"

"I'll say. Since I last saw you, we've moved into a better apartment. I got an unexpected bonus check from my last client. And I got a new ghostwriting job a little over a week ago. Dale Davenport ended up hiring me after all. Heck, even Mary got a job at a high-end jewelry store in the city."

"No kidding? You've had a productive three weeks. Good for you, son. I didn't even know Mary was looking for a job."

"Well, she's always been looking, but she seemed to get more serious about it a few weeks ago when she told me her next goal was to find a job in a place that would appreciate her talents."

Dave's mouth was full, but he managed to get out, "That was a good goal to set."

"She's been very goal oriented lately, ever since we moved into the new condo. I think Matt's wife, Caroline, has been influencing her. She seems happy, and that's all I care about."

Dave sat up straight when he heard Caroline's name. "Is this the Caroline Fresno that Matt was dating? They got married, right?"

"Yeah, well she's Caroline Mooney now since the wedding. How do you know her maiden name?"

"She was one of my students when I taught philosophy at Worcester State College. She was in my metaphysics class and really took to it."

"No way!" Robby was surprised he hadn't known about this. He actually hadn't ever known that his father taught a metaphysics class.

"She's a bright girl. I encouraged her to teach her own class when she graduated. I remember that she really took to the principles of intention back then. I wonder what she does now." Dave took another bite of his sandwich.

"I'm not sure, to be honest," said Robby. "I know she helps Matt out at the store. But he often mentions her teaching workshops about something. I've never paid too much attention to what that is. Maybe it's goal setting because Mary seems very goal focused nowadays."

"Are you sure she's not intention focused rather than goal focused?" asked Dave.

Robby laughed, not realizing that his father was being serious. "I don't think Mary knows about setting intentions, Dad."

Dave suspected that Caroline had taken his advice. *She must be teaching her own practical workshops on intention rather than teaching the subject academically at the college*, he thought silently. *Clever. I wish I'd thought of doing that.*

Dave's thoughts were interrupted when a plate hit the floor behind him and wobbled to a stop. An elderly woman using a walker had tried carrying her tray up to the trash bin on her own and was now sprawled out on the floor. Silverware and napkins were spread across the floor, and the woman was sitting in a pool of spilled water from her overturned cup.

Robby jumped up to help her. The woman was laughing hysterically at herself.

"Are you all right?" asked Robby.

"You can dress me up, but you can't take me out," she said and giggled.

"Are you sure you're not hurt?"

"My pride may need surgery," she said, "but I'm fine if you'll just help me up."

Robby and Dave helped the woman to a standing position. While Dave made sure she was stable, Robby picked up the tray, plate, silverware, and empty cup. He used the napkins to clean up what little water hadn't already soaked into her bathrobe.

"Oh, thank you. I thought I could balance it, but this walker is still new to me."

"I'm just glad you're okay," Robby told her while he made his way to the receptacle stand to throw away the trash and put the dishes in the bin.

The woman looked at Dave. "Is that your son?"

"He's all mine."

"You raised him right."

"I can't take the credit, but thank you. I'll probably keep him. He can walk you to your room if you'd like."

"I can manage as long as I'm not juggling anything," she said, laughing. She thanked Robby and Dave and slowly left the cafeteria.

"Son, you just witnessed the secret to a happy life."

"What's that? Walking with a walker?"

"No. Not taking yourself too seriously. Did you see the way she laughed at herself after falling and sitting in a pool of water?"

"I did. She had me laughing."

"Just keep her in mind the next time you take a spill in life—and I'm not just talking about falling on your keister."

"I get it. That really was pretty amazing. She's a good example for the rest of us."

The father and son watched the woman as she slowly made her way out into the hall and waited for the elevator.

"So finish your story about Mary. What's this new job she got?" asked Dave.

"Right. So she told me about her goal of getting a job where her talents would be appreciated. Next thing I know, she ran into some lady she knows, Eva something or other, who works at that jewelry store Mary loves that's been in Greendale for like forever. Eva told her that the clerk they had working there was quitting. They needed someone in a hurry and Eva thought Mary would be perfect for the job.

"So far she loves it. Most of the time she works with Eva, whom she adores. The owner's a bit of a grump. I've only met him once. But he's making jewelry in the basement most of the time. She even gets a fifty-percent discount on all the jewelry. Mary's thrilled. It was quite a coincidence how it all happened so quickly after Mary set her goal."

"Do they appreciate her talents like she intended?"

"Yeah! The owner's teaching her how to design jewelry, and she's loving it."

Dave put the pieces together in his head. *Let's see: First, Caroline, a student of mine from years ago who had a knack for the principles of intention, is now teaching workshops of her own. Second, she's been teaching her friend Mary what she knows. And third, Mary "coincidentally" gets the exact job she desires soon after she learns what Caroline teaches her.* He was sure he knew what was going on, but it was also obvious to him that Robby didn't have a clue.

Robby and Mary must both be using the power of intention to create the realities they desire, yet neither one knows the other is doing it. Dave found the situation comical. Still, he knew it wasn't his place to connect the dots for Robby. He trusted that his son would put the picture together himself when it was meant to happen. Aloud he said, "That's pretty amazing, son. I'm happy for you both."

"Thanks, Dad." Robby cleaned up the last drops of ketchup with the final bite of his sandwich and then ate the remaining potato chips on his plate.

Dave took a deep breath like he was full and packed up his tray. He looked at his watch. "Nurse Betsy said it would be a while longer before my release papers are ready. Let's just sit outside for another few minutes. I've spent way too much time on the third floor. I'd rather wait out in the sun."

"That's fine. There's a door over here."

They put away their trash, trays, and utensils, and walked outside. They were surprised to see a sitting area outside the cafeteria. There were six picnic tables on a red brick patio. Two of the tables were occupied with nurses, men and women, some smoking cigarettes.

"If we had known, it would have been nice to sit out here," Dave commented.

"Except for all the smoke. You know, you can light up if you want, Dad. I won't give you a hard time."

Dave laughed. "The last butt I had was the one you saw me smoke three weeks ago. I didn't get better this quickly by smoking cigarettes. To tell you the truth, now that I've quit, the smell of cigarette smoke is enough to make me lose my lunch."

"You want to leave?"

"No, I'm fine. It's such a nice day."

One of the nurses looked at her watch, and suddenly all six people in blue, pink, and purple scrubs packed up their belongings and walked inside. Dave and Robby moved to one of the tables where the nurses had been sitting because it was the only table with sun on it. They sat quietly on either side of the picnic table, basking in the rays for a few minutes.

Robby remembered that he had something he wanted to ask his father. "You were right last time I was here, Dad. I don't want to be writing books for other people anymore."

"I can understand that."

"I'm feeling it more than ever. Dale keeps cancelling our scheduled interviews, which could possibly turn this six-month job into a yearlong job if he keeps it up. And I have a feeling he's used to doing whatever he wants no matter how it affects other people."

"I've heard that some celebrities can be that way, son."

"It's not just Dale's behavior. Ever since I've been practicing the mala, I keep getting a line of people who want to hire me to ghostwrite their books. That's great, I know, but it's not what I want anymore. Now that I know my mala practice works, how can I use the mala to make a living writing my own books instead of writing them for other people?"

"You're really feeling it, huh? I mean, the itch to write your own books?"

"I have for a long time. Until this year, however, I pushed that dream down, not believing it was possible. Truth be told, I loved ghostwriting the first few times I did it. But now that I've seen what is possible using my mala, I have a glimmer of hope that I might actually be able to live my original dream. That tiny bit of hope set loose a desire inside of me that now aches to get out. By not pushing it down anymore, I have realized that it's really more of a need than a desire.

My soul-level craving to express myself has been the source of a low-level depression for too long."

Dave leaned his arms on the table in front of Robby. "That's a powerful realization."

Robby continued. "My heart and soul have longed for the creative fulfillment of writing my own books, yet my ongoing belief that it wasn't possible—at least not for me—crushed that longing, so I remained in a self-inflicted prison where I wrote other people's books rather than my own. I now see how cruel I was being to myself, and quite frankly, Dad, if I don't find a way to fulfill my dream, I'm afraid of how this unfulfilled expression will manifest in my health and my relationships. I believe it could lead to a chronic depression."

"That's a life-changing insight, son—and what a perfect example of what happens when we go from sleeping through life to self-awareness. Fortunately, you've realized this early in your life. I believe I can help you. Tell me, what's the intention you set and what mantra have you been using with your mala?"

"I just set the intention to attract more abundance into my life, more money. And this is the mantra I've been using." Robby pulled the mala booklet out of his pocket and showed his father the Sanskrit abundance mantra he'd been using.

Dave read the mantra out loud. "Om shrim maha Lakshmiyei swaha. I always liked that one." He handed the manual back to his son. "Well that makes sense. You've been asking for abundance, which you've been getting, but you haven't guided Creative Intelligence to what form you'd like that abundance to take. You need only make a simple adjustment that I call 'being more specific with your intention.'"

"You mean I should invent a more detailed intention?"

"Exactly. Creative Intelligence actually prefers it. And you can do this in a few different ways. First, you can just think about, or tell someone, the details of your intention. What's most important is that you know the specifics, so listing them in your mind or telling someone verbally is sufficient.

"Second, and a more effective method, is to write down exactly how you'd like your intention to look, feel, smell, taste, sound, and be. If your intention is to attract a publishing contract, for example, write down what publishing company you would like to publish your book, what the title of your book will be, and what your book is about. Go so far as to write how much you want for an advance, what percentage of the profits you desire, and how long the contract will give you to write your book."

Dave stared blankly in thought for a few seconds and then continued. "Always end your detailed intention with, 'This or something better.' You never want to limit the Universe. Plus, you might be limiting yourself depending on your beliefs, so intending 'This or something better' gives Creative Intelligence your endorsement to go beyond your own imagination."

"I like that idea," said Robby.

"Third, or in addition to the first and second methods, you can write each detail on a note card or sticky note. This way you can spread out all the note cards on your desk, or stick the sticky notes to a wall, and really get a visual in your mind of all the elements of your detailed intention."

"That's a cool idea as well, Dad. I like being able to see everything in front of me in that way. It helps me remember it."

"The more details you give the Universe, the more likely it is that you'll get exactly what you want. Whenever you leave a detail out, the Universe has to guess on that particular. If you allow this to happen, you'll get some version of your intention, but it probably won't come out exactly the way you'd prefer it to be."

"I see," Robby interjected. "It's kind of like choosing a vacation destination. If I just drive in the direction I want to go, I'll get in the right vicinity but not necessarily reach the exact address I desire to go. But if I find the exact location I want on the map and circle it, I'll go to that exact spot. Is that it?"

"I think you've got it. What's wonderful is that you have already used your abundance mantra to attract greater wealth with remarkable success. So you've proven to yourself that your mala practice works—and in only a few weeks to boot. Now you just need to take it to the next level. It's time to make adjustments to fine-tune your intention and give it more elements. And by doing that, you'll tell Creative Intelligence exactly what you want, not just sort of what you want."

Robby took out a tiny notepad and pen and began writing down some notes on what his father had just taught him.

"Do you always keep a notepad with you?"

"I have to. I'm always thinking of ideas for my books, and if I don't write them down I forget. Right now I'm just making notes about what you said."

"Honestly, I don't think you'll forget. Keep it simple, son. The last thing you want to do is make it complicated."

Robby took his advice and put the notepad in his back pocket. "Okay, Dad, I understand about adding to my intention. What I don't understand is how to take what I've written and turn that into a new mantra to use with my mala. Isn't all that detail too long for a mantra?"

"You bet it is. And that's a great question. You can continue to use the same mantra you've been using or create a new one, but now you merely need to think of what you wrote in detail when you repeat your mantra one hundred and eight times using the mala, which will happen naturally.

"Because you've already thought about the details, even written them down, you know the particulars of your intention. You don't need to repeat every detail over and over. You could decide upon one word that represents for you what you wrote in detail, and that would be all that is required. For example, you could say 'book' or 'book deal' to represent the intention to get a publisher for your novel. As long as you know the full meaning of the intention that your one-word mantra represents, Creative Intelligence will read your mind, so to speak."

"I love that idea, and I look forward to extending the details of my intention. I'm going to do it tonight," said Robby.

Dave looked at his watch. "Want to see if my release forms are ready at the nurse's station?"

"You bet!" said Robby.

Dave and Robby walked through the cafeteria and into the hall to the elevators, which they rode to the third floor. At the third floor nurses' station, Dave said his goodbyes to his nurses, Paula, Betsy, and Sarah. Paula gave Dave a big hug wearing a sad face.

"You're going to miss me, huh?" he asked her.

"Oh sure, like those ten pounds I lost last year," she teased, not wanting to admit she liked his company.

"Listen, Paula, I appreciate all you've done for me around here. It was really nice of you to arrange for Father Burke to take me to the chapel."

Paula kissed him on the cheek and scurried down the hall.

Dave and Robby left the hospital and found Robby's truck in the parking lot. Robby threw his father's suitcase in the back of his pickup and drove them down Route 295 through Worcester, then on Route 195 toward West Boylston where Dave lived. Dave loved seeing the trees, fields, and farms along 195.

"Dad, can I ask you a question?" said Robby.

"Sure, son, anything."

"Why didn't you teach me any of this before? I'd probably be a lot further in my life now if you had."

"First of all, life is not a race, Robby. It's simply an experience. If you're experiencing life, you're on the right track. This includes negative experiences along with positive ones. Nobody is moving in the wrong direction. Everyone is exactly where they should be at every moment."

"Okay. But that's not what I asked."

"I know, but it's important enough that I had to say it first. Now, second, as I told you a few weeks ago, you never asked. Of course, I know that's still not the answer you're looking for. In all honesty, the main reason I didn't teach you this stuff earlier is because you weren't open to it."

Robby cocked his head back, looking at his dad.

"Hold on, son. Don't be offended. You know it's true. Ever since you took that journalism course in college, you've seen yourself as a skeptic. And since you wouldn't accept anything you couldn't prove with evidence, you were never open to considering what I've been teaching you lately. Metaphysics is all about the unseen—the invisible. The truth is, I approached the subject with you a few times and you were always quick to dismiss it."

Although Robby was a little annoyed, he knew his father was right. He regretted asking the question.

"To answer your question: You weren't ready because you didn't believe. Your mind was closed to discovering the truth. The fact is that one doesn't have to believe to discover the magic of the mala and intention. One only needs to be open to different possibilities.

"Said another way, one needs to admit that one doesn't know everything. Sometimes we need to fall on our heinies in life before we're willing to admit our limitations and open our minds. That's certainly your story more recently, and it's an age-old story, so don't be embarrassed. You're in good company. Plenty of people have done the same thing."

Dave patted Robby's thigh with a look of pride as Robby drove. "You're only thirty-two years old, son. You're way ahead of the game in comparison to me at your age. I didn't wake up until my early forties. A lot of people don't have their awakenings until much older. And still others never wake up to their ability to create with their thoughts, words, and actions, which is fine, too, although life gets a lot easier when we do."

Robby drove into his father's driveway feeling a bit humbled. Only a moment ago he had been feeling frustrated with his father for not telling him about the mala sooner. Now he realized that he only had himself to blame. He was realizing that in the last few minutes he had gone from feeling frustrated with his father, to feeling regret that he had asked his father why he'd withheld his wisdom from him, to now feeling gratitude that he had opened his mind to this subject at all.

Gratitude, he thought to himself. *It sure feels a whole lot better than frustration and regret.* With that splendid realization, he shut off the engine of his pickup truck and carried his father's belongings into the house.

CHAPTER SIXTEEN:
THE WORKSHOP

MARY WALKED INTO the Marriott Hotel. The front desk was on the right, a bar to the left, and a couple of high-end shops straight ahead. As her eyes adjusted from the bright outdoor sun to the darker interior, she noticed a sign just inside the door that read: *The Intention Workshop – Room 113*. With the help of a Marriott employee, she found the room located across from the indoor pool.

Inside the room were about thirty-five people, mostly women of all ages and a few middle-aged men. Mary found a seat in the back. At the front of the classroom stood Caroline, who was preparing some papers at the podium. She was looking sharp in a light blue jacket, white blouse, and a knee-high skirt that matched the jacket. She looked up and saw Mary, and immediately walked to the back of the room to say hello. "I'm so glad you came," she said as she hugged Mary. "I really think you're going to get a lot out of it."

"I'm happy to be here. How are you doing?"

"I always get excited before I give a workshop. Hey, how would you feel about sharing your story about getting evicted and then finding that super awesome condo you now live in? It's a great example of how intention works."

Mary squirmed in her chair. "Really? I don't know. I've never spoken publicly before."

Caroline stared at her, pouting.

Mary gave in. "Okay then, I guess. Will you help me out if I crash and burn?"

Laughing, Caroline assured her she'd be great but that she would definitely be there for her if she needed it. She gave Mary's shoulder a squeeze and ran back up to the podium to begin the workshop.

Caroline began by telling the story of how she and Matt had used the power of intention and attention to go from broke to financial security in just a few years. She explained that what she was about to teach was thousands of years old and not some new-fangled fad.

"The techniques we're here to explore have been called New Thought, the Science of Mind, and the Law of Attraction, but they are both none of these things and all of these things together. The big-picture reality is that these techniques are the basis of physical manifestation, which always begins with thought.

"What you're about to learn is not solely about money or material possessions. These same principles can be used to improve your health and your relationships, attract more happiness into your life, and even have more inner peace. However, I will talk mostly about money and material manifestations for a couple reasons. One, almost everyone wants more money, right?"

The people in the audience agreed.

"Two, attracting more money into your life is a practice that quickly teaches you if you're utilizing the principles properly. It's the perfect measuring stick to see if what you're doing is working.

"Three, once you've mastered using what I teach in this workshop to create more money, you'll automatically know how to use these principles to fulfill any other desire."

Caroline explained intention and attention just as she'd taught Mary a few weeks prior. Then she introduced Mary. "My friend here has one of the most extraordinary stories exemplifying the power that intention and attention holds for each of us. She's agreed to share her story with you here today. I ask that everyone listen with respect and gratitude since Mary will be sharing some very personal and emotional experiences. Okay, the floor is yours, Mary."

Mary stood up and began telling her story. At first she spoke softly and her voice cracked a few times. Yet the further she got into the story, the stronger her voice grew. By the time she was done, several women and one man in the class were wiping tears from their cheeks. At the end, everyone gave her a standing ovation and people around her were thanking her.

Once everyone was seated again, a man in his sixties raised his hand. Caroline responded, "Yes, Tony?"

Tony stood and said, "The speed at which Mary created her intention, read her affirmation, and then learned about the bulletin board notice regarding the condo for rent seems lightning fast. I'm not being skeptical. I'm just wondering, how do we know when something is real or when it's a mere coincidence?"

"That's a fantastic question," said Caroline. "Let's not forget that Mary also took action when she joked to the waitress about wanting a new apartment with her hot fudge sundae because the action in her story is significant as well. But to answer your question . . . when we set an intention, write it down in detail like I taught earlier, turn it into an affirmation or a mantra—which are basically the same thing—

and then take action toward the manifestation of that intention, all this together is us communicating to the Universe. That speeds things along.

"I also like to think that we each have our own guardian angels or spirit guides that assist us during our lifetime, so if that image works better for you use that instead. Just keep in mind that those guardian angels or guides are working in partnership with the Universe using the same laws of energy that we're discussing."

Caroline moved out from behind the podium to stand closer to the students in their chairs. She looked at the people seated, one at a time, as she spoke. "Tony asked about coincidence. I personally don't think of coincidence in the way most people refer to it. I can only speak from what I know using my own direct experiences. Intention and attention are our ways of communicating to the Universe. We've already discussed that. What I haven't taught you is that the Universe also communicates back to us. It does this in four different ways."

She waited while several people grabbed their pens and pads to begin taking notes. When they seemed ready, she continued. "The first way the Universe communicates to us, or guides us, is through coincidence. Now some might call this serendipity, synchronicity, or divine coincidence. But what it is not is mere happenstance or a fluke. When two or more events occur that have no obvious relation to one another yet result in a meaningful connection or result, that is a sign from the Universe to pay attention.

"Coincidence requires our awareness to notice it, first, and also some interpretation on our part, second. The coincidence might be the Universe's way of making us pay attention to something else that is happening or being said in that moment. For example, you might be talking about calling your mother and—BLAM!—an acorn hits your windshield like a bullet. If that happens, I'd definitely call your mother."

Several people laughed.

"The coincidence might also be the Universe's way of putting emphasis on an important message. If you cross paths with a friend who tells you she's going to an intention workshop, then your father mentions an ad he saw in the local paper about the upcoming intention workshop, and then you drive by a sign in front of the Marriott that reads 'Intention Workshop Today,' I believe that's a strong signal that you're supposed to attend that workshop."

There was more laughter from the classroom.

"We're talking about present-moment awareness here. When you focus on what's happening in front of you at the moment, rather than focusing on what happened in the past or what might happen in the future, you're going to be more open to—or aware of—the messages the Universe is putting in your path."

Caroline walked from the right to the left side of the room, looking people in the eyes as she asked, "Does everyone understand coincidence being one way the Universe communicates to us?"

People nodded. A couple of voices quietly said, "Yes" and "Yup."

"All right then, the second form of communication, or guidance, that the Universe sends us is messengers. Messengers are often people, but they can also be animals and insects, and yes, even spiders and snakes. Messengers deliver messages from the Universe either directly or indirectly.

"So if your eight-year-old son tells you that you need to drink more water, don't just assume he's repeating something he heard from somebody else. In fact, it wouldn't matter if he did. If that's something that is unusual to come out of your son's mouth and you notice it, pay attention. You might be dehydrated and at risk of getting sick. That could be a direct message from the Universe.

"I know a woman who really needed to come up with some money and didn't have a clue as to how to do it. Behind her on the bus one day, she overheard another woman talking on her cellphone saying that she'd just sold her unwanted gold jewelry for three thousand dollars at a place that buys gold. Well, the woman who needed money just happened to have a box of unwanted gold jewelry sitting in her closet, but it would never have occurred to her to sell it if she hadn't overheard that comment. The woman on the phone who was sitting behind her on the bus was a messenger from the Universe. And, again, this was a direct message."

A dog barked outside the hotel window, interrupting Caroline. She pointed toward the window. "We've all heard stories about dogs barking incessantly at their owners to warn them about some danger, be it a stove fire or their spouse collapsed in another room. When I was young, our dog barked to alert us that someone was attempting to steal our car at three o'clock in the morning. My father jumped out of bed, turned the lights on, and yelled at our dog to stop barking, which scared away the thieves. Boy, did my father feel bad the next morning when he realized what had happened."

The audience laughed.

"Lives have been saved by animals of all sorts because people were aware enough to pay attention to the messages they sent. The animals in all these cases were messengers.

"Because animals can't speak our language, most of these types of messages are considered indirect messages. For example, I know a woman whose dog got a certain type of cancer. Once the owner learned the symptoms of that type of cancer from the veterinarian, the woman rushed to her own doctor. She'd been having the same symptoms and had been ignoring them. Sure enough, she discovered she had the same form of cancer. She might not have caught it early if not for her dog. And she's okay today, several years later. Her dog lived to an old age as well."

Caroline paused and looked around at people's faces.

"That last story makes you think, doesn't it? Well, there are a lot of examples to indicate that our pets will sacrifice their own lives to help us. One day we will all understand that animals are more advanced spiritual beings than we are. I certainly know it's true for the dogs and cats I've owned. It requires advanced-level beings to do what they do for us and never get credit.

"Not to confuse you, but to better show you how this works, the earlier example I gave you about the Intention Workshop . . . well, the friend who said she's going to the workshop and the father who read the ad about the workshop from the newspaper are both messengers. They were messengers, and it was the coincidence of you getting the same message three times that really nailed the message home. So that example used a combination of messengers and coincidence—two of the four ways the Universe communicates with us.

"So what's the third way? Anyone know?" Caroline scanned the room for someone who might know.

A meek voice in the audience squeaked out, "Intuition?"

"Yes! Excellent," Caroline said as she pointed in the direction of the person who spoke. "The third way the Universe communicates to us—or guides us—is through our intuition."

Caroline's enthusiasm for the subject was visible in her body language. She hopped in the air, walked up and down the aisles of the classroom, and communicated with her hands.

"Everyone has intuition. I'm not talking about psychic ability, although psychic ability really is just an enhanced type of intuiting. Your intuition is nothing more than your inner sense about things, your gut feelings or personal instincts. It's that spontaneous thought or feeling that pops up in your mind and body. Yes, even in your body. You have an entire nerve center in your stomach area where you receive intuitive messages. It's called the enteric nervous system, or second brain. Hence the term *gut instinct*.

"It's extremely important that you learn to trust and pay attention to intuitive signals because much of this is guidance from the Universe, or if you prefer, from your guardian angels."

She stopped mid-aisle and looked around at everyone.

"You all understand that I'm using the phrase the Universe, but we can replace that phrase with God, Infinite Intelligence, Source, Higher Power, and Creative Intelligence to mean the same thing, right?"

A few people nodded.

"We're referring to the divine energy that connects every person, animal, and living organism in our cosmos. I just want to make sure no one is confused by it, okay?"

A few people responded affirmatively. Some were still writing on their notepads.

"There's one more way that the Universe communicates with us, and it's the least obvious one. Anyone know it?" Caroline looked around the room and waited. There were no takers.

"It's events: things that happen to us or around us. I sometimes refer to these as 'divine events.' For instance, you might get fired from your job only to land a more enjoyable job with better pay. That's what happened to Mary. She got evicted, which led her to find a much better place to live."

Caroline walked back up to the podium and looked at her outline, then said, "Or your boyfriend or girlfriend might break up with you, which might lead to a new relationship with someone who is more loving and compatible with you. Or to give one more example, you might break your ankle and begin writing a novel you've always dreamed of writing, which might become a *New York Times* bestseller."

The students were frantically writing.

"Those are all great examples, but this type of communication from the Universe isn't always going to be a seemingly negative event like breaking a leg or getting fired. It can also be wonderful events. I had a woman in one of these workshops who found a wallet and ended up marrying the man who owned it. Another example is how I was once given tickets to a conference where I met someone who became one of my closest friends.

"We could call these coincidences, but in fact, they are events because the initial cause and the later effect have a lot of space between them. Even more clearly, you'll recognize events by the way they alter the direction of your life.

"Life-altering events typically only happen when we are not listening to the other three types of communication from the Universe. They are God's way of turning us around to go in a direction that is more likely going to align us with what we desire from life. So if we become aware of the guidance of coincidence, messengers, and intuition, there tends to be less need for the major events to occur—especially the negative ones that reset our course—which is a good reason to start being more aware of the other guidance, right?"

Everyone agreed.

Caroline looked at her watch, then said, "In summary, we communicate with our spirit guides or higher selves by setting intentions and giving those intentions our *attention*. What we focus upon expands because the focus of our thoughts sends out an energetic vibration—a frequency—that is matched by the Universe, which comes back to us like a desire-gifting boomerang. In essence, our thoughts become our reality.

"Then, because the Universe is responding to our intended outcomes, it works with us to make them happen. How? By guiding us . . . by putting the right people and circumstances in front of us to help us meet our goals. Thus, we need to pay attention. We need to remain aware of the signs and signals that the Universe is sending, which may come in four forms: One, coincidences. Two, messengers. Three, intuition. Four, events.

"The more alert we keep our awareness of possible communication, the better able we will be to use guidance to expedite the manifestation of our intentions."

Caroline threw her pencil and paper down on the podium and sighed loudly. "Phew!"

The group laughed.

"Let's take a short break. We'll meet back here in twenty minutes."

The students started talking to one another as they left the classroom. A few people rushed up to Caroline to ask questions, so she responded by saying loudly for everyone to hear, "We'll take questions after the break. For now, let's give our minds a rest and move our bodies."

The line of people in front of her quickly dissipated with a few moans. Caroline walked over to Mary unaffected. "That was amazing," said Mary. "You're such a great teacher."

"I'm glad you enjoyed it. You want to get some fresh air?"

"Sure, but then I have to go to work. I'm going to have to miss the second half," she said.

"No problem. I'll let you know what you miss later. I told you I'm happy to give you private lessons."

The two walked out the door as Caroline began praising Mary on how well she'd told her story.

CHAPTER SEVENTEEN:

THE MEDITATION

DAVE WALKED INTO Mechanics Hall and was immediately in awe of its beauty. Behind the stage sat a floor-to-ceiling organ that was as fine a centerpiece for the eyes as it was pleasing to the ears. Dave looked at the pamphlet that came with his ticket: "The Hook Organ, appropriately named because it was built by Elias and George Hook, was installed in 1864. It's a fifty-two-stop, 3,504-pipe organ, and the oldest unaltered four-keyboard pipe organ in the Western Hemisphere."

Dave looked around and saw Father Burke looking over the balcony railing above him. He found his way upstairs to see the view with the minister from above. The men greeted one another with hugs.

"You got your ticket at Will Call, I see," said Dave.

"Yes, thank you for this. This is such a joy. You know I've never seen Benedictine monks in concert, but I listen to Gregorian chants quite often in my chambers and find them relaxing."

"Me, too. I listen while I meditate. Don't be surprised if I go into a trance state during the concert," Dave kidded. "The second my brain hears this stuff, I go into another dimension."

"I've seen that already at the hospital chapel. One time you were levitating three feet off the ground," Burke kidded back. "Which reminds me, I've been meaning to ask you something. I hope you don't mind, but the speed at which you healed was astounding. When we first met, you had pneumonia and whatever else was causing you to barely be able to move from your bed to a wheelchair. Can you tell me how you turned your health around so quickly?"

"Of course, Father. But you probably already know what I'm going to say. The day we met, you pretty much described having an experience that was quite similar to mine. At its core, I begin every meditation with a prayer, which I call an intention. I ask God to infuse me with his power to heal.

"I then imagine a golden light coming down from the heavens and entering my body through the top of my head. In my mind's eye, I see that light pouring in and filling my body with God's healing energy. With every in-breath I take, I imagine my body filling up. With every out-breath I take, I imagine exhaling any toxins or disease from my body."

Burke absorbed every word Dave said, nodding his head to indicate he was listening.

"I continue this visualization until I can feel my entire body vibrating—buzzing—like you shared with me from your own experience. As I breathe, I visualize each part of my body filling with golden light, one body part at a time.

"I begin with my head and work my way downward. First I feel my scalp relax and heal, then my ears, eyes, nose, mouth, and chin. I then feel my neck relax and heal, and then I feel the warmth of God's light move into my shoulders and arms. I continue slowly moving through my body by visualizing my biceps relaxing and healing, then my triceps, my elbows, my forearms, my wrists, my palms, the tendons in my hands, and my fingers.

"At this point, I usually feel my fingers, but sometimes my entire hands, go numb—not in a bad way, like when someone gets frostbite, but in a positive way. I take it as a sign of relaxation. My fingers begin to tingle and feel very light. I then visualize and feel healing light moving into my chest, my stomach, and then traveling all the way down my back. From there I visualize the light moving into my hips and reaching down into my thighs. A sense of relaxation pervades every area the light touches.

"I take my time. Only when my thighs are completely relaxed and buzzing with light do I move into my knees, and then my calves, my shins, and down to my feet. Again, I slowly imagine the relaxation and healing light moving through my heels, the bridges of my feet, the bottom of my feet, and then into my toes. By the time I reach my toes, my whole body is often buzzing with energy."

Burke had his eyes closed while he listened.

"It's at this point that I visualize my entire body being healthy. I imagine myself doing activities that healthy people can do, like walking down the street with ease, running in a field with joy, swimming in a lake, and playing outdoor games with my future grandchildren.

"I continue to visualize myself in perfect health doing fun, physical activities until my mind eventually goes blank and drops into the space between thoughts and breaths. This place is what you might know as the God space. And I remain in this state until something or someone awakens me out of my meditative ecstasy."

Father Burke shook his head back and forth in awe. "And that's how you healed yourself from barely being able to get out of your bed to walking around Mechanics Hall like a young man again?"

"That's it, yes! After only a week, I was walking around my room. After two weeks, I was walking around the hallways of the third floor. And in the third week, I was walking to the courtyard on the first floor by myself."

Burke pointed at Dave with a smirk. "To have a cigarette?"

Dave laughed. "No, I haven't had a cigarette since the day I met you. I gave that up after my wife came to me in my dream."

"It's truly amazing how quickly you recovered."

"I'm still improving. I have a ways to go yet. I'm not ready to go jogging. I would lose my breath too quickly. But I'm a new man without a doubt."

"You've certainly showed me what's possible," the minister admitted. "I've never seen a recovery like yours."

"I surprised myself. Granted, I had years of practice with this method of meditation before my wife passed away. I wasn't meditating for healing back then, however. In those days, I was visualizing career success, loving relationships, and solutions to everyday problems. You can use meditation of this sort to support any intention you desire—by breathing the intention into every part of your body. I just happened to use it for health most recently."

"That's truly inspiring, my friend," said Burke. "I wish I had witnessed this twenty years ago."

People were beginning to take their seats in the hall, so Dave asked, "Do you want to find our seats?" The friends made their way downstairs.

"I'm glad you gave up the smoking," Burke whispered to Dave as the house lights began to dim and the audience grew quieter.

"Yeah, that was a means to an end that no longer served me," Dave whispered back. "And I'm sure my wife doesn't mind waiting for me a little longer."

The men laughed softly together as the monks began to chant.

Dave fully enjoyed the chanting. The acoustics in the hall sent the monks' voices reverberating through his entire body. He closed his eyes within minutes. About a half hour into the chanting, Dave's whole body began vibrating. He leaned back in his chair and opened his eyes to see a chandelier hovering above them. A movement caught his attention, and then he couldn't believe what he was seeing. His wife, Margaret, was sitting on the chandelier looking down at him. He closed and reopened his eyelids, then took another look.

"Yup," he said to his wife silently in his mind. "It's you. You're sitting on a chandelier. Any particular reason why?"

"I just wanted to get your attention."

"Well, you certainly did. I don't understand, though. I'm not sleeping. How is this possible?"

"Your conscious mind has gone into a semi-sleep state due to all the meditation you've been doing. The monks' chanting triggered it since you listened to their music during your meditations. You're actually seeing me in your mind's eye. Come on up. Join me here on the chandelier. You won't believe the view."

Dave closed his eyes and imagined sitting next to her. In an instant, he was there. "The view really is extraordinary. They should sell seats up here," he joked.

"Yes, and there you are sitting down below next to your friend, the minister."

Dave looked down and saw himself. "This is disconcerting. No one is going to believe this when I tell them."

"I don't recommend telling people. They'll put you away for good," teased Margaret.

"Can anyone see us up here, Margie?"

"No. I'm really not able to explain it, but no one can see us."

"Then how am I able to see you?"

"You aren't seeing me with your eyes. You're seeing me with your third eye. That's what meditation can do for some people. It opens up your third eye, which is the conduit between the physical and the spiritual dimensions. Because you used to meditate for years before my accident, it was easy for you to go deep in meditation after just a few weeks of practice in the hospital. It's why you were able to heal so quickly."

"Will I remember this later?"

"You will. You'll always remember this as if it just happened, even years from now. But you'll question whether or not it was real, so take my hand."

Dave held Margaret's hand and was surprised by how real it felt. The instant he touched her, his eyes filled with tears of joy. It felt better than the best embrace they'd ever had when she was alive. He could feel the love she felt for him. It was the most intense love imbued with immeasurable compassion and joy all at once.

Hand in hand, Margaret and Dave floated through the walls of Mechanics Hall, which felt to Dave like pushing his way through mud. Margaret then floated Dave around the city.

"I can still hear the monks chanting," Dave said, surprised. Margaret smiled. She took Dave on a tour over Lake Quinsigamond in Worcester where they used to swim before Robby was born, past St. John's High School in Shrewsbury, which Dave attended as a boy, up to the Wachusett Reservoir in Oakdale where Robby and Mary lived, through West Boylston over Dave and Margie's house, then over Hope

Cemetery in Worcester where Margaret's body was buried, and back toward Mechanics Hall.

When they reached Mechanics Hall below them, a crow flew up to Margaret. As the crow hovered in front of her, flapping its wings, Margaret gently plucked a black feather from the bird's body. The crow bowed its head to Margaret and gracefully flew away. Mary took Dave in tow back through the walls of Mechanics Hall to where they finally sat on the organ bench behind the Benedictine monks who were still singing.

"Wow, that was remarkable," Dave told Margie.

"I thought you'd like that."

"What a memorable tour. And I'll never look at a crow the same way again. Are you going to give me the feather so I'll know this really happened later?"

"Yes, but not now. Take a good look at it so you know exactly what it looks like," she said as she handed it to him. Dave held the feather with one hand because he didn't want to let go of Margaret's hand with his other. The feather was about three inches long and jet black with a one-inch streak of white near the top. He observed it closely and handed it back to his wife.

"There is one person you should share this with. You need to tell Robby. He'll be more open to it than you would imagine because I also visited him in his sleep. Most importantly, you must describe the crow's feather to him so he can believe, too."

"I will, my love."

"And keep doing what you're doing, honey: keep teaching Robby what you know. He's new to this, but he will become a great teacher one day who will share this wisdom with millions."

"I will, Margie."

"It's time to go now. I love you, David." Margaret kissed Dave on the lips, which sent a bolt of love through every cell in his body. He instantly found himself back in his chair seated next to Father Burke. He remembered everything that happened, but he wished he could have asked her more, especially about the crow's feather. He did his best to put his questions aside and trust that everything would be answered when it was meant to be. He leaned back to enjoy the rest of the concert, still vibrating with the loving energy that remained from his wife's kiss.

CHAPTER EIGHTEEN

THE CONFUSION

O N THE ADVICE of his father, Robby had written down a new, more detailed intention. It began with gratitude for the blessings he had already accumulated, like Tru had suggested he do at the library, and then included his detailed vision for being a successful author writing his own books. Just as his father had instructed, he included all the details of how he hoped that would look, feel, and be. Finally, he abbreviated that into a simple two-sentence mantra that read, "Thank you for the blessings. I am a wealthy and successful author writing my own books."

Robby practiced his mala with this new mantra for a couple weeks. As he did, he found himself whistling around the house, accomplishing household chores with joy, and even noticing the beauty of nature more, such as the birds outside the condo and all the flowers that Jenny had planted around its perimeter.

One morning, immediately following his mala practice, he called his current ghostwriting client, Dale Davenport. They had scheduled an interview to discuss elements of Dale's book and Robby was hoping Dale hadn't forgotten the appointment again.

Dale's wife, Sue, answered the phone.

"Robby?" she answered, recognizing his number from the caller ID.

"Hi, Sue. Are you crying? What's the matter?"

"Robby, Dale died last night." Her words were barely understandable beneath the crying and sniffling. "We think he had a heart attack. He just didn't wake up. I got out of bed to make us coffee, and I thought he was asleep. When I brought him his coffee, I realized he was gone." She sobbed in a fit of grief.

Robby was in shock but pulled it together enough to console Sue as best he could. He expressed his condolences and then hung up as quickly and kindly as he was able. His entire body was shaking. He fell into a fit of panic after hanging up.

Oh my god, I'm responsible for Dale's death! he thought. *My intention to stop ghostwriting and begin writing my own books gave him a heart attack.*

Robby had seen so much immediate success with his original mantra for more money that he believed his more detailed intention must have been powerful enough to cause Dale's death.

Nobody warned me that I could harm someone doing this! he thought as he felt a frenzy of emotion well up inside of him. His chest became tight, and he felt short of breath. He became lightheaded and lay down on his office floor.

I should have known this was dangerous stuff to be fooling around with, he told himself. *It was too good to be true. Nothing good comes without a price.*

After twenty minutes of doing deep breathing while lying down, he managed to stand up again. He was still shaking and his stomach was in a knot, but he wasn't dizzy anymore. He grabbed his mala from his desk, looked at it with grave disappointment, and then threw it into his office wastebasket. *Who was I kidding? I can't believe I allowed myself to play with this new age stuff. My father needs to know the danger that he's putting people in by teaching these ideas.*

Robby decided to find his father and tell him what he had done to Dale. "I'm not taking the blame for this!" he said out loud as he grabbed the keys to his truck. "This is on you, Dad. And you've made me an accessory by playing with your magic."

He got into his pickup and started the ignition, still mumbling to himself. "Just follow these steps and you can write your own books, Robby. Sure, Dad, look where it's got me now!"

Filled with fury, he drove to St. Vincent's Hospital, parked his pickup truck, and stormed to the elevator. While he was waiting for the elevator, Father Burke saw him through the doors of the chapel. The minister walked out to the hallway. "Robby? Is that you?" the minister said.

Robby wasn't feeling sociable, but he didn't want to be disrespectful. "Hi, Father Burke. I have something I need to talk to my father about," he said sternly.

Burke sensed he was distraught. "Son, you took your father home a couple weeks ago, remember?"

Robby was so used to visiting his father at the hospital that he'd automatically driven there. The elevator dinged, the door opened, and Robby stepped toward it but then stopped himself. His mind was overwhelmed by his emotions.

"Oh my god, I'm such a dope!" he said out loud.

Father Burke gently took his arm and walked him into the empty chapel where they could have some privacy. They sat down at the first pew they reached.

"Is everything all right, son? You know, I'm a good listener."

Robby couldn't look him in the eye. "My father gave me some advice that led me to do something that ended up being harmful. He needs to know that his beliefs are dangerous."

The chaplain chose his words carefully, realizing how angry Robby was with his father. "I've only known your father for a short time now, but I feel like he's been pretty forthright with me. He's never shared any beliefs that seemed harmful from what I can tell. Do you want to be more specific?"

Robby reached into his pocket for his mala and remembered that he had thrown it away. "Do you know what mala beads are, Father?"

"Yes. We have our own version of them. We call them rosary beads." Father Burke pulled on the rosary beads he wore around his neck to display them. "Is this what you're talking about?"

"Yeah, but the mala doesn't have a cross on the end, and it has a lot more beads."

"Yes, my rosary has thirty-three beads, one for every year of Christ's life. Catholic rosaries have fifty-nine beads. But I've seen what you're talking about."

"Well, my father taught me to think of an intention and write a mantra to summarize it. He then told me to repeat the mantra once for every mala bead."

"We do that, too. We call it prayer. It's sort of a to-MAY-toe to-MAH-toe thing. Go on."

Robby got a little annoyed with the minister. He was trying to explain his father's ill-fated ways and Father Burke kept interrupting and neutralizing everything he said.

"Well, my father told me to set an intention to make a living writing my own books rather than writing books for other people, and I did it."

Burke waited patiently for Robby to continue, assuming there had to be more.

"I did that for a couple weeks, and this morning my client died. I'm afraid that I might be responsible for his death, which would make my father responsible for it because he encouraged me to do it."

Father Burke was happy to have the mystery solved. His body relaxed as he saw that he would be able to help the young man.

"I see. So basically you prayed to God to be able to earn money writing books of your own. This would mean you no longer wrote books for others. And because your client died—now giving you time to write your own books—you're worried that God took your client's life in order to grant your wishes."

Robby thought the summary sounded a bit simplified, but he couldn't argue against it. "Yeah, I guess that's it."

"Your client wanted to write a book as well, am I right?"

"Yes. That's why he hired me."

"So by hiring you he indicated his own prayer—or intention—to complete his own book."

Robby nodded in agreement.

"In fact, son, it was probably also your client's prayer—or intention—to live longer than he did. Is that fair to assume?"

Robby nodded again. He realized a wise old man was dismantling his argument.

"So if your conclusion is correct, God not only chose to grant your prayer to write your own book over your client's prayer to write his book, but God chose to grant your wish to write your own book over your client's wish to live a longer life. Thinking of it that way, do you think God favors one person over another so deeply that He's willing to end one person's life to give a boost to the other person's career goals?"

"But my mala exercise had worked so well before. Was that just a coincidence, too?"

Father Burke put his arm around Robby's shoulders. "I'm not sure I believe in coincidence, son. You've heard the question about which came first, the chicken or the egg, right?"

Robby nodded.

"We'll never know for sure, but isn't it possible that God inspired you to pray on your mala for the career change you desire because He knew your client was soon to come home to Him? Isn't it within God's means to see the opportunity for you to begin writing your own books soon, so He put that desire in your mind?"

Robby listened intently, tears sliding down his cheeks.

"Perhaps God was just getting you to think in new ways before your client died so that you didn't just immediately take a new client when his death occurred."

Father Burke took his arm off Robby's shoulders and placed his rosary beads in Robby's hands. "I've been doing this for a long, long time, more than all the years you've been in this world, and I've never seen a prayer intended to improve someone's life negatively affect the life of another. Prayer only works from love. I'm talking about love for every man, woman, child, and animal. It is literally impossible to use prayer to benefit yourself to the detriment of another. God's infinite wisdom knows how to answer your prayers in a manner that works for all humanity."

Robby sat quietly for a few moments. As he did, the muscles in his face and body changed from tense to relaxed.

"Look, Robby, your father is an insightful man with great wisdom to share with you. And he isn't just a wise teacher, he also walks his talk. Pay attention to your dad, especially these days. He's a different man than he's been for the last few years."

Robby sat up straight. "I'm glad I came here . . . by mistake," he said with a hint of a smile. "I guess it wasn't any coincidence that I did. Thank you for being so patient with me."

He gave the minister a hug, handed him back his rosary beads, and they said their goodbyes.

Robby walked out of the hospital and sat in his truck in the parking lot for a while watching people come and go. He contemplated how he must have been led to Father Burke by a higher power, considering that he, himself, was the person who'd driven his father home after his release from the hospital. He thanked God for His guidance, knowing that Father Burke was perhaps the only person who could have explained what he had with the perspective Robby needed at that moment. When he felt ready, Robby drove home to pull his mala beads out of his wastebasket.

CHAPTER NINETEEN:

THE REFLECTION

ROBBY AND MARY finished eating dinner at their favorite Irish restaurant in Worcester, Murphy's Restaurant and Bar, to celebrate their fifth wedding anniversary. They had a more formal dinner planned with friends to celebrate on the weekend, but they wanted to do something on the actual day of their anniversary. The pub was quiet and familiar, and a place they both enjoyed. Plus, it was the restaurant where they'd had their first date.

Robby ordered the same dish he always got, shepherd's pie. Since Mary didn't eat meat, she ordered a big salad with warm goat cheese and beets, golden delicious apples, and romaine lettuce.

They paid their bill and were walking out when they ran into an old high school friend named Stan Barone. Stan had been at the bar for a while already but was returning after going outside for a quick smoke. Robby and Mary wanted to get home, being that it was eight thirty at night and Mary had to work in the morning, but Stan insisted that they come back inside and have a drink with him to catch up.

Stan was thirty-two years old, though he looked like an unhealthy fifty-year-old. He was thin in every manner except for his protruding beer belly. His skin was thin and had a reddish tint to it. His hair was thin and greasy. His face was thin with a long nose and chin. Even his legs and arms were thin, which was especially noticeable due to the mechanic's uniform he wore that was a couple of sizes too large for him.

Stan had gone straight to the bar right out of work, so he was a few drinks ahead of the Robinsons. "You guys look great. You really do," he said as Robby and Mary settled in at the bar. "You must live a good life."

"It's so good to see you, man," Robby said in return.

"How is everything?" asked Mary. "Are you married yet?"

Stan laughed. "No way. I can't be tied down to no ball and chain. Ahh, no offense, Mary. I mean, I was seeing a girl for about a year, but she was on my back about this and that, so I dumped her."

"Oh, that's too bad, Stan," said Mary.

"Yeah, she had all these dreams of doing this and that—of owning a house and getting married. I told her, dreams just set you up for disappointment, you know? It's not good to get your hopes up because then you're just sad if they don't work out. Why be sad when you can be happy without dreaming, like me? I say, live in the moment. Am I right?"

Stan lifted his beer for a toast. Mary and Robby forced a half-hearted reciprocal raising of their glasses. The couple shared glances, both thinking the same thing: *What did we get ourselves into?* Stan was too intoxicated and self-focused to notice.

"I see you're still a mechanic," Mary said in an effort to divert the conversation. "Are you still working at Lander's Garage?"

Stan made an exaggerated wave, indicating no. "I haven't worked there in a long time. They fired me. They said I complain too much.

I can't help it if they don't know what they're doing. I have to speak my mind, you know?" Stan guzzled some of his beer while talking. He sounded like he was talking underwater. "So I got a job at the gas station down the street. What a dump that place is, and I told 'em so. They didn't like that, so they fired me. I'm working at the muffler shop now on Gold Star Boulevard. It kind of sucks, too, but it's a paycheck. You know what I'm saying?"

Robby could see why Stan's life was a mess. He thought about what Tru had taught him in the library. *If you think happy thoughts, you'll attract happy people and circumstances into your life. If you think unhappy thoughts, you'll attract unhappy people and circumstances into your life.* Robby realized that Stan mostly thought unhappy thoughts, and then he empowered those thoughts by saying them out loud. Robby tried to change the subject again to lighten up the conversation.

"How's your mom, Stan? I haven't seen her in five years."

"My mom? Oh, she's good, I guess. She got the cancer a few years back, but I guess she's okay now. I had to give her a ride to the doctor the other day 'cause her car broke down. That car was always a piece of crap. Right from the start, that car never ran right. I told her when she got it that those cars suck, but did she listen to me? No way. Nobody ever listens to me. So now I have to drive her to the doctor because she didn't listen. I should charge her for gas, you know? It's not like my truck gets good mileage or nothing. I probably only get ten miles to the gallon."

When Stan stopped talking to drink his beer, Mary stood up from her chair and said, "We really have to get home, Stan. I have an early morning. I hope your mom is going to be okay."

Robby was right on cue and helped Mary with her jacket. Mary gave Stan a hug goodbye and quickly walked away. Robby told Stan as he shook his hand, "Yeah, Mary's got to work early tomorrow. Listen, man, take care of yourself. Say hello to your mom for me, will you?"

Stan started mumbling something about not planning to see his mother anytime soon if he had any say about it, but Mary and Robby were already making their way out of the bar by the time he finished his sentence. Stan moved his empty glass from the table to the bar and ordered a refill from the bartender.

The bartender asked him, "Are your friends leaving so soon?"

"I know, right? I was hoping they'd buy another round. But nooo, she's got to get up early," he said in a mocking voice. "Lightweights."

Happy to have escaped Stan's incessant complaining and negativity, Mary and Robby sprinted across the restaurant parking lot and hopped into their station wagon like they were making a getaway after a bank robbery. Both laughing, they leaned against one another like school kids.

"Oh my god," said Mary. "I was just having a conversation with Caroline about people who say one negative thing after another. She was saying how we have to be really careful about the words we say because we're putting that focus out into the Universe. The thoughts we think and the words we speak are like seeds that grow in our future."

"Someone was saying the same thing to me a few weeks ago," said Robby, thinking of Tru. "We were talking about people who are always complaining or talking about things they're worried about."

"Oh my god, Robby, Stan is the perfect example of how negative thoughts and words create negative experiences. It's an energy that, once you get caught in it, perpetuates itself."

Robby nodded in agreement. They were no longer laughing, and instead were now feeling compassion for Stan.

"That could have been me," said Robby. "I was on my way there just two or three months ago. Heck, do you remember how negative I was in the months prior to us getting evicted?"

"You were never that bad, Robby, probably because you don't drink like Stan. Our bodies can recover rather quickly from an occasional drink, but Stan is going to have a difficult time raising his level of consciousness enough to improve his life if he continues to lower his physical and mental energy with so much beer."

Robby sat in silence thinking how Stan had helped him open his eyes to his own past behavior. Sure Robby didn't drink much alcohol, but he did talk a lot about how unhappy he was writing books for other people rather than writing his own books. *It's no wonder I wasn't getting any new clients*, he thought. *My acidic attitude must have chased them away.*

Mary interrupted Robby's thoughts, mirroring her husband's epiphany. "Did you feel the repelling force of everything Stan was saying? I couldn't wait to get out of there. Another minute and my brain might have exploded from listening to all that gloom, hostility, and cynicism."

"I was just thinking the same thing. Maybe that's what I was doing when I wasn't getting any new clients. Maybe my unhappy thinking was repelling them."

Robby was fascinated by the truth of what Mary recognized in their experience with Stan. Negativity really did have a repelling effect. Then it occurred to him what she'd said. "Hey, wait! I didn't know you had so much insight into this subject, Mary."

"Well . . . I guess this is a good time to tell you. I've been learning from Caroline," she admitted. "She gives workshops about using our thoughts, words, and actions to claim the life we desire. Did you know she does that?"

"I knew she gave workshops, but I thought she taught goal setting," he said, laughing at his mistake.

"I attended one of her workshops, and she's an amazing teacher." Mary's eyes widened as she realized what was happening. "Oh my god. I can't believe this, Robby. I had no idea you knew anything about this stuff either. How long . . . when—?"

Smiling, Robby said, "Do you remember that time you went grocery shopping with the last of our money?" Mary nodded. "It all started that day."

"Why didn't you tell me?" she asked.

Robby took a deep breath. "Well, if I'm being honest with both you and myself, I didn't say anything for two reasons. First, I was just dipping my toe in the water—testing it—and I didn't want to tell you until I made up my mind about it. Second, and more likely the reason I procrastinated saying anything to you, I was too embarrassed to tell you considering how outspoken I've been about not accepting anything that can't be proven. You'll be happy to know that my father has really helped open my eyes about how my skepticism has held me back over the years."

"Wow, you're kind of blowing my mind here. You know, I'm glad you waited to tell me because my enthusiasm might have pushed you too fast, leading you to stop testing altogether. So, tell me, are you familiar with the concepts of intention and attention?" asked Mary.

"Intention, yes. Attention, no. What's that?" Robby started the station wagon to go home. The entire drive, Mary taught him what she'd learned from Caroline about the importance of giving our intentions attention, and how our actions are a form of attention. When they got home, Robby showed Mary his mala. He realized they both had a lot to teach one another.

Mary could not have been more excited to learn that Robby had finally opened his mind to metaphysics. She was also excited to learn about the mala, immediately recognizing that it was a powerful tool for giving attention to an intention.

"Now we can do our metaphysical exercises together," she suggested. "What might be possible if we worked together on the same intentions? I wonder if the results would be exponential?"

The two stayed up late in bed telling each other the many stories they had been keeping from one another over the last couple months. Ironically, they both had Stan and his negativity to thank for bringing their passions so close to the surface that they couldn't keep them secret any longer. Mary taught Robby how Stan was an indirect messenger for them and then taught him the four ways the Universe communicates with people that she'd learned from Caroline.

Before going to sleep that night, they both expressed gratitude to the Universe and Stan for bringing the truth of their independent intention practices to light. Now that they weren't hiding their intention exercises from each other, they would be able to share anything new they learned along the way. That night, Robby and Mary made love with more intimacy then they had in months. It was a wonderful ending to their fifth anniversary.

CHAPTER TWENTY

THE LIMITATIONS

ROBBY DROVE into the bookstore parking lot. Matt had called to tell him he was going and invited Robby to join him. Since Robby wasn't working following Dale's death, he was glad to take the opportunity to spend some time with his friend. Matt was already inside when Robby arrived.

Robby found his friend in the self-help section. Robby thought it funny to see Matt in a bookstore, period, but he really thought Matt looked out of place in the self-help section. "Hey, what's up? I expected to find you in the sports section," he told Matt.

"Hey there, Pinhead. I do have other interests, you know." Matt was looking at *The Life-Changing Magic of Tidying Up* by Marie Kondo.

"Tidying, really? I've never seen you as a tidy kind of guy."

"Yeah, well maybe that's why I need this book," Matt replied while he continued reading. "To be honest, I really appreciate her idea of keeping what brings you joy and discarding what doesn't. We could apply that to a lot more than just decluttering our homes. I'm going to apply it to people, too. Imagine spending more time with the people in your life who make you feel joyful and less time with the people in your life who drain your energy like vampires."

Robby saw another copy of the book on the shelf and picked it up. "You know," he said, "we could also apply it to things we do, like those obligatory events we feel we have to attend but hate going to. You know what? I've just made a decision: as of right now, I'm no longer attending events that don't bring me joy."

Matt looked up from reading his book and considered Robby's idea. "What about a child's birthday party or a graduation? Those aren't very fun, but you still have to go to them. Are you not going to attend those?"

"No, I'll go to those because it gives me joy to celebrate important moments in my loved ones' lives. They might be on the dull side, but I still get joy out of seeing the happiness of others who are celebrating their birthdays or graduations. What I'm going to boycott are events that don't bring me any joy, like an invitation from toxic people who talk about themselves for two hours and never ask about your own life. By the way, did I tell you we ran into Stan Barone recently?"

Matt laughed. "Don't even say it. I ran into Stan myself a while back. You just described him to a tee. Oh my god! Can that guy vomit negativity all over you or what? I felt like crap after talking with him for only fifteen minutes. It totally threw off my day."

Robby nodded in agreement. "That's what I'm talking about. Okay then, thank you Marie Kondo. We just applied your brilliance of decluttering and organizing to fit other areas of our life as well. That's my new litmus test: will this bring me joy? I love that idea."

After a few minutes of perusing books in the self-help section, Matt wanted a coffee at the Starbucks inside the bookstore. The two men got their coffees, Robby got a slice of pumpkin bread, and they found a table where they could sit and chat.

"I've been meaning to ask you, Robby. Next month, there's a sports memorabilia convention in New York City I need to attend. Would you like to tag along?"

Robby took in a deep breath and exhaled slowly through his puffed-out cheeks. "I'd love to go, but I shouldn't spend the money. I'm not even working right now."

"That's why I'm inviting you, Dingleberry! Doesn't New York City have publishers all over the place?"

Robby shot him a testy look. "Yes, but that's not how it works. You have to mail or email them a book proposal and then wait and wait and wait. I mailed mine a couple weeks ago. Now all I can do is wait."

Matt nearly choked on his coffee. "Are you kidding me? Caroline told me you've had a new awakening. But you talk like someone who's never learned about metaphysics in his life."

"What do you mean? I'm doing my mala practice twice a day. I've written out every detail of what I want. I'm even watching my negative self-talk."

Matt pushed Robby's shoulder. "You're such an amateur. All right, now listen carefully." Matt moved his chair closer to Robby so he could talk softly. "Everything you just said to me is a limiting belief. You said: 'You have to mail them a book proposal.' 'You have to wait and wait and wait.' Those beliefs are limiting your success, and they're obviously limiting the action you're willing to take to achieve your dreams. You need to raise the ceiling on what you believe is possible because it's holding you back, man."

Robby listened quietly. He couldn't respond because he knew his friend was right. Still, he'd been told by others and read in many books everything he knew about getting published. It was difficult to believe there was an alternate path.

"I could also find a literary agent to represent me," Robby added, "but I've been told it's equally as difficult and nearly the same process to get their attention."

"What might you do if someone hadn't convinced you that the only way publishing companies or agents accept book proposals is through the mail or email?"

Robby thought about it. "I don't know, maybe I'd call them instead?"

"Yeah, maybe. Or maybe you'd realize that we live in a world that favors relationships over talent. Do you think it's possible that some new authors get publishing contracts just because they know somebody at the publishing company? In other words, they might have some talent, but don't you think that some writers with less talent are getting published because of who they know, while some more talented writers aren't getting contracts because they don't know anyone? Do you think that happens?"

"Sure, it probably happens all the time."

"Okay then, so it's time to think. Do you have any connections with an editor at a publishing company?"

Robby shrugged his shoulders like he couldn't think of anyone.

"Didn't someone just send you a five thousand-dollar bonus because they got a publishing contract? And didn't that person say the publisher loved your writing?"

"Oh, right! You're talking about Samuel."

"Yeah, Samuel. And don't you have other ghostwriting clients who got publishing contracts with books that you wrote?"

"Okay, okay, I get it."

"You're such a beginner," said Matt. "Do you understand that what you do speaks as loudly to the Universe as what you say or what you think?"

"Yes, in fact, Mary just taught me about attention and action. I think she learned about those ideas from your wife."

"Then I don't have to ask if you've been writing that book that you want to get published?"

Robby slouched and bit his lip.

"Look, Pantywaist, what you do or don't do sends a message to the Universe about what you truly believe at your core. If you hope to get published but aren't spending any time writing the book yet, you're sending a mixed message. Don't you think?"

Robby interrupted. "But I've heard that publishers prefer you don't write the book before they accept the book proposal. They prefer to guide you on how they want it written."

Matt lightly slapped him on the back of the head. "Did you just hear yourself? Who taught you that limiting belief? What I've heard is that publishers prefer to work with agents who have clients who know how to write books. Who has the time to babysit authors on how to write their books?"

"Honestly, I don't remember who told me that. I just thought that's how it works because I've never been on that end of a book deal."

"And were they talking about fiction or nonfiction books?"

"I'm not sure. I assumed they meant both."

"Did it ever occur to you that every autobiography you ghostwrote for one of your clients was written before it was sold to a publisher? Am I right?"

"Yeah, you're absolutely right, but autobiog—"

"Don't you dare tell me that autobiographies are different because what would that be if you did?"

"A limiting belief," answered Robby with a grin.

"So what are you going to start doing?"

"Write my book."

"Unbelievable. And you're the one who got all As and Bs in school," sputtered Matt as he stood up to get a refill on his coffee.

Robby knew Matt was right. He had been sitting around waiting to hear from the publishing company rather than taking further action to help the project along, including beginning to write it. Plus, now he had the time to write it because Dale had died and Dale was his only client. He recognized he had a lot more to learn about metaphysics in addition to practicing his mala. Until now he'd had no idea how much his limiting beliefs were holding him back.

Matt returned with two coffees. "You're going to need another coffee for what I'm about to tell you." He sat down and thought about where to begin. "Are you familiar with the concept of beginner's luck?"

"Sure. Who isn't?"

"Well, most people are familiar with it, but most people don't know *why* it works. Do you?"

Robby thought about it but was pretty sure he didn't have a clue. He shook his head no.

"A beginner succeeds for a while because his head isn't filled with lots of reasons why he might not succeed. A new poker player doesn't realize the odds against getting a full house or a straight flush. So all he does is imagine winning and he does. A beginner's belief is that the game is purely fun and easy to win. So a beginner wins, so much so that I will never play for money with a beginner. Often he doesn't even know he's winning. He'll get a straight flush and ask, 'Is this good?'"

Robby laughed.

"The Universe gives us what we see in our mind's eye, nothing more and nothing less. The Universe is one hundred percent detached from what it sends our way. It mirrors the vision we send out to it without any regard to how that might affect us. Why? Because it's merely delivering what we ordered with our thoughts, words, and actions. And why do we order anything less than what we desire?"

"Because of our beliefs," answered Robby.

"That's right. If you've been taught all the reasons why getting a publishing contract is difficult, all those obstacles now cloud your vision. Especially if you've never been published before—because you're more open to accepting what other people tell you in that case—you weigh their opinions more heavily than your own. The obstacles that people told you exist have created a filter between your desire and what you are actually getting. And all the obstacles that you learned are now your beliefs about what's possible."

Robby had his notebook out and was taking notes.

Matt continued. "Our beliefs become a filter that alters the potency of our vision and our intentions. They are what stand between us and the manifestation of our desires. Robby, you constantly need to challenge your beliefs by asking yourself: Is this my belief of how this works or is it something that I learned from someone else, which I accepted as true? Was it believed due to a past experience I had that made me think it is true? Or is this belief the result of something I read in a book or saw in a movie that I accepted as true? If the answer to any of those questions is yes, you need to challenge those limiting beliefs. With practice and awareness, you'll start to hear yourself the moment you say a limiting belief out loud."

Robby interrupted. "Can you give me some examples?"

"Sure. I used to say, 'I'm not good at math.' Where did I learn that limiting belief? You say, 'I'll never be able to make a living writing my own books.' Who suggested that to you? 'Publishing companies have their rules, so I have to follow them.' Who convinced you that following the rules is always the best route to success?"

Matt paused and took a swig of his coffee.

"Frankly, Matt, you're right," Robby admitted. "I say those things to myself all the time. I think my entire life has been affected by limitations I've accepted from one source or another."

Matt patted Robby on the back. "You're preaching to the choir, man. We all do. The trick is in recognizing them and then questioning those beliefs. Now listen closely because I've got something that will blow your mind. Have you ever noticed that the kids we went to school with who had wealthy parents typically ended up affluent? And that the kids with middle-class parents tended to end up being middle class? Or that most of the kids with poor parents ended up in a very similar financial situation as their folks? People refer to this phenomenon as 'the apple not falling far from the tree.' Do you know why that happens most of the time, even though there are some exceptions?"

"Because it takes money to make money?" Robby guessed.

"You see, that's another limiting belief, just like 'We have to work hard to get ahead in life' and 'The rich get richer, and the poor get poorer.' No, Biscuithead, the reason kids typically end up in the same socioeconomic stratum as their parents is because they only know what they know. Said another way, they don't know what they don't know."

Robby recalled his father saying something similar to him in the hospital.

Matt continued. "If you can't imagine yourself living in a million-dollar home, driving a luxury car, or wearing designer clothes, the ceiling you've created for yourself is due to the limitation of your own experiences. How can we visualize what we don't know?"

Robby nodded in agreement. Matt was making a lot of sense to him.

"Kids who grow up in environments that we consider wealthy automatically see themselves in a similar environment as they grow up. This affects how they choose their careers, what salaries they ask for when applying for jobs, and what goals they strive for their entire lives. It's natural for them to visualize themselves being wealthy because that's all they've known all their lives. They grew up in a wealthy environment.

"But kids from lower socioeconomic households don't have any concept of what it feels like, looks like, smells like, or tastes like to be wealthy. So unless they have friends whose parents are wealthy, most of what they know about affluence comes from television or magazines, which feels more like fantasy than reality to them.

"What do you think they visualize when they dream about improving their lives? Do you think they dream of owning a Rolls Royce, a BMW or maybe a late-model Chevy? Do you think they see themselves living in a mansion or a nice three-bedroom colonial with a two-car garage? Do you think they dream about earning millions or do you think they dream about earning fifty thousand dollars a year? Do you see where I'm going with this?"

"Yes, and it makes perfect sense," said Robby. "But what's the solution if we don't know what we don't know?"

"Well, because we don't know what we don't know, most of us do a little better than our parents. We're apples that don't fall far from the tree. We see what people in our same-but-a-little-better economic level have and do, and we visualize those things when we dream about our future. We're able to visualize the house a slightly richer friend grew up in or his father's slightly nicer car. Or we may choose to be a lawyer because our rich friend's mother was a lawyer, or an accountant, or a sales manager, or whatever."

Robby chimed in, "So this is why most people improve only in small increments during their lives rather than making major leaps?"

"Precisely. Major leaps are possible, but this is one of the main reasons why it happens less often. It's not just because life is set up with advantages for some people—no way. It's largely because of our beliefs. Our beliefs are directly connected to what we know and what we've experienced. If we can believe something is possible for us, we can set an intention to be it, have it, or do it. If we can set an intention, we can achieve it with our thoughts, words, and actions. Manifestation is a creative process. The truth is, we usually only take action if we believe the action will bring us a result we want. Therefore, every intention is limited by what we believe, and our beliefs are affected—for better or worse—by our experiences."

"So in order to make giant leaps forward, we need to discover what we don't know?" asked Robby.

"You got it. This is why motivational gurus like Tony Robbins have been recommending for years that we surround ourselves with people who are more successful than we are. There are a lot of reasons why this is a smart practice, but the foundation is that we learn what we don't know just by being around people who are living the lifestyle that we wish to live."

Robby's mind was spinning. Neurons were firing in his brain, making new connections like never before. He was feeling a sense of clarity about what had been holding him back. "I've been so ignorant," he confessed.

"We're all ignorant about something, dude. Let me give you an example about what I've been talking about from my own life. Whenever I used to get a client who had to fly me out to appraise some of their sports memorabilia, it was in my contract that they had to pay for the plane fare. I did that for a couple years until Caroline and I went with her parents on a cruise to Mexico. Well, her parents paid for the flight and upgraded all of us to first class using their credit card points. That was the first time in my life I experienced what it was like to fly first class. Before that I didn't know what I didn't know. It's not a whole lot different, if I'm being honest, but the larger seats, extra legroom, better food, nicer service, and free cocktails certainly made the flight from Boston to San Diego a whole lot nicer."

"I'll have to take your word for it," Robby teased.

"So what do you think is the first thing I did when I got home from that vacation? I altered my contract so it said my clients had to pay for first-class airfare. And guess what? For the next three years, not one client ever blinked an eye at flying me out first class. Nobody complained. Nobody tried to negotiate it down to coach or business class. My new flying experience has improved how I feel about making these trips. I used to dread them, and now not so much.

"Before that vacation to Mexico, I couldn't imagine flying first class. I didn't know what it was like, and I didn't feel worthy of asking my clients to pay for it. But once I experienced it, and I saw that everyone else in first class was no different than me, it changed my paradigm so that I was able to visualize nothing less for myself."

"That's incredible," said Robby. "So are you buying us first-class tickets to New York City?"

"No, Jabba-the-putz. We're driving. But I'm glad you're coming."

CHAPTER TWENTY-ONE:
THE PROGRESS

DAVE ARRIVED to pick up Mary for her lunch break. He walked into Jankowitz Jewelers and was immediately surprised at how elegant it appeared inside. It was an unexpected contrast to the unadorned brick exterior.

A lush Oriental rug lay over an oak floor in the customer area. Pairs of plush upholstered chairs waited in the far corners opposite the counters. The display cases were framed in cherry wood that had been polished to perfection, and the glass above the jewelry was spotless, covered only with crystal bowls filled with pink foil-covered chocolates that beckoned to be eaten.

Mary stood behind the counter waiting on a customer. "You were here last week with your niece, right? Eva helped you."

The woman smiled. "Yes. I live in New York City but visit my sister every summer. My niece and I come here every year to add a charm to her bracelet. I think this was her seventh. This year she chose a tennis racket charm. She recently won a tournament."

"Did you get to watch the winning match?" asked Mary.

"I did. It was a nail-biter. I'm very proud of her."

"I'll bet you are. And this pearl necklace, is this for you?"

"Yes. I'm being presented with an award back home this fall, and I like to buy my jewelry here when I can."

"An award, huh?"

"Yes, it's no big deal, but it gives me a reason to dress up."

Mary laughed softly. "Well, congratulations."

"Thank you. I think I'll go with this necklace here." The woman pointed to one of the necklaces Mary had laid out on the display case.

Mary pulled a pair of earrings from the case. "I'll tell you what . . . if you'd like to get these matching earrings, I can give you twenty percent off their price."

The woman hesitated in thought.

Mary added, "The necklace and earrings came in together last week. Can you see how the color differs from these pearls over here? It might be difficult to match the set later. And, besides, you should treat yourself. This sounds like a special occasion."

The woman waved her hand. "Oh, wrap them both up. You're right; I deserve it."

Mary placed the necklace and earrings in boxes, processed the sale, and handed the woman her bag of items. "Thank you, Ms. Horowitz. Have fun at the awards ceremony."

"I will, dear. Thanks for your assistance."

As the woman left the store, Dave took notice. He walked up to Mary and said while still watching the woman walk out the door, "Wow! Who is that?"

Mary giggled. "That's Ruth Horowitz. Eva told me last week when she was in with her niece that she's been coming here for years."

"She's a classy lady," said Dave. "Any idea what her award is for?"

"No, she didn't seem anxious to say, and I didn't want to pry." Mary walked around the counter and gave Dave a hug. "Thanks for coming."

"Of course, sweetheart. What a beautiful store. Give me the tour."

Mary proudly escorted Dave around the store while he ate some of the pink-foiled chocolates. Since Mary had been with Robby for fifteen years, Dave was like a father to her. She pointed out the most expensive jewelry to him, the jewelry she thought was the most beautiful, and the mala beads she and Eva had personally strung.

"I didn't know you sold mala beads here," Dave said.

"We didn't at first. I recommended it to Mr. Jankowitz, and he purchased five malas made from gemstones when he was in Boston. We sold out in a week. After that, he taught Eva and me to string them ourselves."

"Are these malas strung with silk?" Dave asked.

"No, silk used to be the first choice for stringing necklaces. It still is for pearls. But today we use synthetic materials like nylon and polyester for most necklaces. These have the same qualities as silk—even look just like it—but they don't stretch like silk, and they hold up better to cosmetics and perspiration. Silk gets dirtier and discolors faster than these new materials. The synthetics are much more durable in strength and color, so you can wash your mala beads now and then without harm. Plus, and I think best of all, silkworms are not killed in order to make the synthetic threads."

"Are you talking about monofilament fishing line? I heard jewelers use that sometimes."

Mary laughed. "No, I heard that, too. These are very soft cords that look, feel, and perform just like silk."

"You certainly are learning a lot by working here, sweetheart."

Mary spoke quietly. "Mr. Jankowitz plays the grumpy old man, but he's actually very kind. He's taught me and Eva a lot."

Mary introduced Dave to Eva and then told Eva she'd be back in an hour. She and Dave walked down the street to Lani's Deli & Sandwich Shop. After ordering their sandwiches, they carried their plates and drinks to one of the outdoor tables with a canvas umbrella.

"I was happy to hear that Robby finally told you about his mala practice."

"Me, too. I believe I have you to thank for giving him his mala, Dave."

"No, not really. I only played a small part. He was ready. He and that mala found each other."

Mary stood up, walked over to a counter with condiments and plasticware, and grabbed some extra napkins. She handed Dave a second napkin as she sat down. "You're going to need this," she said. "These sandwiches are delicious, but they're kind of messy."

Dave waited for Mary to get herself settled before he began eating.

"Robby told you about his dream, too, huh?" asked Mary.

"Yes, his mom, Margie, has now visited us both in dreams."

"I heard about your experience at Mechanics Hall. That sounds amazing."

"I'm not sure Robby believed me, but his mother wanted me to tell him about it."

"I think he wants to believe these were true visitations. He's come a long way, but it's a big jump for him to go from believing in the power of intentions to believing in an afterlife."

"Trust me, I know. I just wish I had found that crow's feather like Margie promised me. I think it would have helped if I could have shown an object like that to Robby. I'm worried that I might have overlooked it. She might have left it on my seat at the concert or something like that. I'm not always very observant."

"You know, he had another dream a couple nights ago," said Mary. "He didn't see Margaret again, but the dream had a crow in it."

Dave stopped eating and looked up at Mary. "Last time, he said a crow woke him up from his dream, right?"

"Yes. This time a crow was actually in his dream."

"Oh, that's a new one. I haven't seen him in a few days. Tell me about it," said Dave.

"He was sitting at his favorite place at the reservoir by the waterfall when a crow landed on the rock in front of him—in his dream, of course. He and the crow just stared at one another. He said it seemed like hours went by and that he'd never felt so at peace. He could feel his mother's presence, but he couldn't see her. All of a sudden, the crow flew away and on the rock in front of him was a black feather. He picked it up and saw it was jet black except for a streak of white near the top, just like the one you described from the Gregorian chant concert. And that was the end of the dream. Pretty cool, huh?"

"That's extraordinary. She showed him the same feather. Holy moly! Maybe that's what she meant she would do after all. What did he think about it?"

Mary wiped her hands and face with a napkin. "He said it was amazing. He said it felt like his mother was right there, even though he couldn't see her—almost as if she was the crow. But his skepticism won't allow him to really believe it was anything more than a dream. He thinks maybe he dreamed about it because you told him your story from Mechanics Hall."

They sat in silence for a few minutes eating their sandwiches. Mary felt sad for Robby that his skepticism got in his way of appreciating such a powerful gift from his mother.

Dave got up to lower the umbrella so they could feel the sun on them. He looked at Mary for approval. "Definitely. Please do," she told him. Dave lowered the umbrella, and Mary closed her eyes and turned her face toward the sun. "That feels great."

Dave sat back down. "So what's going on with you, Mary? How are you doing?"

"I've been good. I was getting a little bored at work, feeling like I needed more creativity in my life. You know that my last job was drawing portraits for people at the photography studio, right?"

"Yes, I remember."

"I loved that job, but my boss was such a jerk that I had to quit it and get out of there. I don't know how I ended up selling jewelry, really. I met the owner when I went into the store to sell something and a few weeks later he offered me a position. I just love being around the beauty of the jewelry. But lately I have been feeling a need to express my creativity again."

Dave listened intently as he ate his turkey on rye.

"I talked with my friend, Caroline, about it. She suggested that I set an intention to find more creative work and wait to see what the Universe delivers. She said that when you don't know how you want something to look, that's a good way to start. So I set the intention and paid attention to whatever signs came my way."

"She's a wise gal, that Caroline."

"Robby tells me she was a student of yours at one time."

"She was. But now I think she could teach me a thing or two. Anyway, go on with your story. Is there more?"

"Yes. About a week and a half ago, this couple came into the jewelry store. Mr. Jankowitz wasn't there that day. The couple were recently engaged, but the man hadn't given the woman an engagement ring yet. He wanted her to design it herself and then have a jeweler manufacture it. She knew what she wanted, but could only describe it verbally. Being an artist, I got out a piece of paper and drew what she described to me."

"Kind of like a police sketch artist," said Dave.

"Actually, a lot like that. In twenty minutes, I was able to draw exactly what she wanted. The woman was really excited. They even offered to pay me for the sketch, but I didn't accept. I was just happy to be able to help them using my talent. I knew Mr. Jankowitz could make it.

"I showed Mr. Jankowitz the drawing the next day and he was impressed, which surprised me because he doesn't get impressed by much. He was really pleased to have a visual of what the couple wanted. He said it would help him give them exactly what they wanted."

"That's amazing, Mary." He pulled out a pen. "Can you show me an example?"

Mary pulled a folded piece of paper out of her purse and began to draw on the back of it. She began drawing an oblong circle and then added some shading to make it appear three-dimensional. She explained the parts as she drew them.

"This is the shank, what most people think of as the ring. We generally begin with a shank that comes from a casting company. There are thousands of different shanks to choose from, so I've been looking through the casting books so I can know what's available when customers tell me what they want."

She drew some gemstones on the shank. "The gemstones, whether they are diamonds, emeralds, or whatever, are held in place by these. We call them heads. The little gold stems on the head that hold the diamond in are prongs. Some shanks have channels in them already from casting, which can hold smaller gemstones. But in this drawing I'm doing here, I'm adding prongs on the side, called the shoulder, to hold the smaller gemstones, or accent stones. All of these top stones together are referred to as the gallery."

Mary quickly drew a circle around her drawing and pushed the paper aside. "There are other parts, like the bezel, stamp, and engraving, but you get the idea."

Dave picked up the paper to get a closer look at the drawing. "That's amazing, Mary. Your artistic talent is obvious, but I can also see how it helps that you know so much about jewelry. And you've learned all this since you started working at Jankowitz?"

Mary nodded while she took another bite of her sandwich.

"Do you think you'll get to do more of these drawings?" asked Dave.

"Oh, right, I almost forgot. So a week later, which was earlier this week, Mr. Jankowitz arranged for three of his clients to come into the store to have me draw a ring, some earrings, and a pendant that they had tried to describe to him at one time. He had never felt confident creating these pieces for them based on their verbal descriptions alone. I was able to draw exactly what they wanted, and Mr. Jankowitz had prearranged with them to pay me seventy-five dollars each for the drawings, over and above my regular salary."

"It looks like you got your message from the Universe."

"Yup, a clear one. I didn't even have to interpret the signs. They were crystal clear. Mr. Jankowitz has two more people coming in later today."

"Your boss seems unusually generous."

"I thought the same thing. It's uncanny. Maybe it's because I recommended that he begin selling mala beads. They're becoming quite popular."

"That's a great story, Mary. You really seem to be able to create what you want in life with ease. Have you and Caroline discussed that?"

"She said that, too, so she asked me a bunch of questions about my life growing up and she came to one conclusion. She said that my parents instilled in me a sense of feeling deserving of good things in my life. She said that a lot of people don't have that."

"She's right, a lot of people lack that quality. It's an internal belief that plagues our society. It derives from the idea that life is supposed to be hard and painful, and that only special people get to be wealthy, healthy, fit, happy, or loved.'"

Dave continued. "It's not that people tell themselves that they aren't deserving. It's more that they ask themselves, 'Who am I to deserve such things?' They feel a sense of shame in expecting comfort and abundance from life, whether in the form of luxuries, love, or just plain good fortune. And this becomes a belief that hinders the successful manifestation of their desires."

Mary finished her vegetarian sub. She and Dave cleared their table and threw the plates and napkins in the recycling bucket. Then they headed back toward the store. "Is it possible to overcome the belief that you're undeserving?" asked Mary as they walked down the sidewalk.

"It can be easier than it might seem. The first step is awareness. Once you know it's there, the second step is to recognize it when it pops up. The moment you notice that you're feeling unworthy or asking yourself, 'Who am I to deserve this?' you must compensate for it by remembering that every single person in this world is equally deserving of every pleasure and pursuit.

"Even though we all came into this world in different bodies and under different circumstances, an abundance of love, joy, safety, peace of mind, and material possessions is equally available to all. In fact, you need not fully believe it to acquire what you desire. If you just open your mind to the possibility that Creative Intelligence doesn't play favorites, you will soon learn that it's true."

"I must admit that I'm grateful that I don't have that particular belief to overcome," said Mary. "I do think Robby thinks in that limiting way sometimes."

"Oh, you bet he does. I'm sure that I'm partly to blame for that in some way. But this work he's doing with his mala is teaching him, little by little, that he deserves to have whatever he wants from life. And you serve as a good example, kiddo."

"Thanks, Dave."

The two stopped midway on an iron bridge and looked into the brook below where a male and a female duck were swimming. They dipped their heads underwater, then came back up and shook the water off.

"So how about you? What's going on in your life? You look amazing by the way," said Mary as they continued walking.

"Thanks. I feel amazing. I'm exercising daily, eating a lot of fresh vegetables, and one important lesson I learned over the last couple months is how vital it is to have a reason to get up in the morning."

Mary asked, "To have purpose?"

"That's right. Any purpose will do. We don't need to save the world. I have had a few friends who stayed alive until their pets died and then died a short time later themselves. Taking care of their dog or cat was enough reason to get them out of bed in the morning."

"That's kind of sad, though, that they died after their pets died."

"It is. They didn't realize their pets were their purpose. If they had, I'm sure they would have found a new purpose for themselves."

"My grandfather died soon after he retired," said Mary. "I always believed it was because he was bored with life. He had no reason to get out of bed, as you said."

"It's more common than you might think. And it's sad because it's completely avoidable. We've been sold this idea that retiring is the American dream, but few people realize that retirement can be boring, which is not a healthy state of mind. We need to replace work with a new purpose. I have retired friends who are thriving physically and mentally just because they play golf a few days a week. Or they have grandchildren who they love spending time with, or they're writing their memoirs. Having purpose is a little secret of life that I've finally learned myself.

"What's your reason for getting out of bed these days, Dave?"

Dave stopped on the sidewalk to watch a young boy who was playing with a toy fire truck. He was leaning over the sidewalk dangerously close to the passing traffic. Dave leaned down so the boy would see him. When he caught the boy's attention, he pointed to the cars going by. The boy's eyes opened wide, and he picked up his toy and walked to the side of the building. He started playing again like nothing happened.

"Well, when I'm not saving little boys from getting hit by cars, I have two reasons for getting out of bed. Initially, helping Robby learn what I have learned in life is what turned me around. More recently I've been teaching patients how to meditate for healing at the hospital."

"No way! How come we didn't know this?"

"Well, I just got started. Father Burke and Paula, one of the nurses up there, helped me put a class together. I have ten people I'm teaching already. I'm having a blast, and my students are already experiencing health benefits from doing meditation."

Mary held Dave's arm as they walked. "You're proof that it works, so you're the perfect teacher for them. What a nice purpose you've created for yourself. You inspire me."

Dave looked up to see they were approaching the jewelry store. "Well, I should probably inspire you to get back to work. You have some people who need your help with their jewelry design. Do you realize that you're helping people make their visions a reality?"

"Hmm, I like that. And they're helping me use my talent in return. It's a win-win."

Mary gave Dave a big hug and kiss on the cheek. "Thanks for taking me to lunch, Dave. And for all you've taught me. You have a lot to share with the world."

"You seem to be doing just fine on your own. The pleasure has been all mine, pumpkin."

CHAPTER TWENTY-TWO:
THE LEAP

ROBBY SAT AT his desk, tapping his pen on the phone. He wanted to call Samuel to ask for a referral to his editor or agent, but he wasn't used to asking for help.

Asking for help is a form of action, he reminded himself. *It helps the Universe help you. The more people we include in our efforts to fulfill our intentions, the easier it is for the Universe to make it happen.*

His stomach ached at the thought of what he was about to do.

It's a limiting belief to think that asking for help is rude or overstepping boundaries. Who taught me that belief anyway?

Robby picked up the phone and dialed Samuel's number. Although he was fearful and wanted to quickly hang up when he heard the first ring, he straightened his body and found the courage to push forward. The phone stopped ringing. "Samuel Thurston's office," said a woman's voice. "How can I help you?"

"Is Samuel available? This is Robby Robinson calling."

"I'll see if he's available, Mr. Robinson."

Robby listened to the music on the line while he was on hold. After a few minutes, he started singing along with it.

"Robby?"

Robby was taken by surprise, hoping Samuel hadn't heard him singing disco.

"Hi, Samuel, thanks for taking my call. How are you?"

"Fantastic. How are you?"

"I'm good, too."

"Oh Robby, I'm glad you called. My book's release is in August. They changed the title like you said they might. However, you should know, they really liked your writing. You're an amazing writer, Robby—my editor said so several times."

"It's nice to hear that feedback because the truth is that I rarely ever find out what happens to the books I ghostwrite."

"You're kidding."

"No. My clients don't usually follow up with me, which I look at as a good sign. People will ordinarily call only if there's a problem. But few ever take the time to give me a compliment—except you, of course. You sent a big check along with your praise."

"You deserved it. And I can give you some more feedback that you might not know. Publishers love you, man. Even my literary agent knew your name. I'm sure you know that two of the books you wrote for your clients hit the *New York Times* Bestseller List, right?"

Robby pulled the phone away from his ear and looked at it. "What? Are you serious?"

"Then you didn't know. How could you not know that?"

"Like I said, I get very little feedback from past clients. I'm not like most ghostwriters. My contract allows them not to put my name on the book, which most of my clients love. And I don't ask for a percentage of royalties, so they don't need to tell me. Plus, since publishers almost always change the title, I don't always recognize my clients' books when they're being reviewed. So what more can you tell me about these two bestsellers?"

"That's really all I know. I can get you the names of those two books, though. I'll email them to you. As far as your reputation goes, my agent said its one factor in why I got the generous advance that I did. It was written by a two-time *New York Times*-bestselling ghostwriter."

Robby's mind was racing. He got lost in thought for a moment thinking he might actually have a shot at getting published.

"You still there, Robby?"

"Yeah, sorry, I just had no idea about any of this. My brain is whirling."

"Are you curious about what I got?"

"Of course. I'm just not so bold to ask. I respect your privacy."

"That's why I like you, Robert Robinson. Let's just say I got back what I paid you and then some. How's that? But keep it between us, okay?"

Robby played with the numbers in his head. *Okay, so my fee was seventy-five thousand, and he got more than that . . . so maybe eighty to one hundred grand? Holy cow!*

"Mum's the word. Thank you for sharing that. It's helpful to me. In fact, it's kind of why I called. I want to start writing my own books, and I was wondering if you could give me some advice on finding a publisher or maybe a literary agent for a book of fiction?"

"Congratulations. I always wondered why you weren't doing that already. Look, I'll email you the name of my agent, but I think he only represents nonfiction books. I'll also give you my editor's name at the publishing company. She's in New York City. You're welcome to tell either of them that I referred you. In fact, email me back if you want me to contact one of them ahead of time."

Robby thought about the coincidence of Samuel mentioning his editor being in New York City since he already had plans to go there with Matt.

He didn't mention where his agent is from, he thought to himself, *only where his editor is located. That's a coincidence that might be a sign, even if only a small one.*

Robby thanked Samuel for his generosity and wished him luck with his book launch.

After hanging up the phone, he was so excited about getting the news from Samuel that he opened his laptop and started working on his book again. Writing his own book gave him an energetic high that few things in life ever did. He hoped that vibrating at this frequency would be helpful in attracting the right agent or publisher.

CHAPTER TWENTY-THREE

THE RECIPROCATION

DAVE STOPPED IN at St. Vincent's Hospital to find Father Burke. He checked the chapel, but he wasn't there. Dave looked over at the pew where he had healed himself with meditation. He felt a surge of gratitude fill his body and got goose bumps on his skin as a tingle ran up his spine.

He went up to the third floor to say hello to the nurses. Paula let him know that the chaplain was attending to a patient who was soon to pass away in Room 305, Dave's old room.

"You know, that could have been me, Paula."

She responded in her loud voice. "Oh, you don't have to tell me. We had bets at the nurses' station on what day you were going to check out."

Dave looked at her in shock.

"I'm just kidding," she said, "but you should see the look on your face right now."

"You got me, Paula," Dave told her. He was a little unsettled, but he knew it was just her peculiar sense of humor.

A few minutes later, Father Burke came out of Dave's old room looking somber. Paula ran back into the room to check on the patient. The minister's face lit up upon seeing Dave.

"You okay, Father?" asked Dave as they shook hands.

"Oh yeah. That's a part of this calling that is meaningful but never enjoyable." He paused. "What are you doing here today? You don't have a meditation class, do you?"

Dave placed his hand on the minister's back, and they walked toward the elevators. "No. I'm here to see you. Is there somewhere private we can go to talk?"

"Hardly anyone goes out in the courtyard. Want to go down there?"

The men took the elevator down to the first floor, making small talk on the way.

"Summer's almost over. Can you believe it?" asked Dave.

"I know. Every time I turn around, it's Friday again. The weeks are flying by, and I've spent most of my days in this hospital. I need to get out more."

The men sat down on the concrete bench in the outdoor courtyard among flowers, ferns, and birds. Burke took a whiff of a butterfly bush that was reaching out toward him. "What's on your mind, David?"

"Well, when you told me the story of how your father left you with your mother's parents after she died giving birth to you, I couldn't get it out of my head. And when you said that you never saw your father again, that you had been told he was homeless and addicted to alcohol, I recognized that I might be able to get some information about him due to my connections."

Burke's head was cocked as he tried to figure out where Dave was going with this.

"Remember how I told you that I owned an advertising agency?"

"Yes, I remember."

"Well, the reason I was able to teach at the college was because I was pretty much hands-off at my agency. The only role I played was to schmooze the big clients now and then. It was my business partner who ran the agency from day to day, and he's the one who bought my half of the business after Margie died."

Burke was leaning toward Dave, hanging on every word.

"Well, he contacted me yesterday. I had called him a few weeks ago because we used to donate a lot of money to the homeless shelters in the city back in the day. He's still involved with those shelters, so he continues to have connections with the people who manage them. He did me a favor and checked to see if anyone with your last name ever comes into the shelters. He learned that there's a George Burke who frequents the shelter on South Main Street."

Burke gasped. "That's my father's name," he said.

"I visited there last night," said Dave, "at the time when George is known to show up for supper, and he was there. I talked with him. He's an old man now, eighty-nine, but he's as sharp as a tack. He's also sober. He lives out of a halfway house in that area."

The minister was staring at the flowers, his hands holding tightly to his knees. Dave couldn't interpret what he was thinking, so he continued talking. "I told him you're my friend and asked if he had any interest in meeting you. He does, quite sincerely. In fact, he cried the moment I mentioned your name and never really stopped the whole time we talked. I let him know that you didn't know anything about me looking for him. And while I apologize if I've stuck my nose where it doesn't belong, I hope you'll know that my intentions come from my heart."

Father Burke's face was now soaked in tears, and his entire body was quivering. He had to gather himself to be able to talk. When he could speak, he looked up at Dave. "My friend, you know me well enough to understand that this is an area of my life where I have craved answers and closure for decades. That's the reason for my weepiness. My shaking hands, on the other hand, are communicating my fear of possibly being hurt again. I felt a hurt so deep that it led me into this calling."

After a pause to catch his breath, he continued. "I think I believed at one time that if I could help others with their emotional suffering, I might in turn help myself. Of course, we're both old enough now to know that it doesn't work that way.

"This is something I've always needed, so I'm thankful to you for what you've done. I'm scared, naturally, but I definitely would like to meet with my father. Quite frankly, I thought that opportunity was gone. I can hardly believe he's still alive."

With that thought, Father Burke let out his emotions. Dave held his friend as he sobbed. When there were no more tears to cry, Dave sat with him while he thought about the prospect of meeting his father.

Minutes later, as they were sitting quietly, a woman wearing a lavender robe walked into the courtyard. She pulled an oxygen tank behind her. A plastic tube wrapped around her head and rested under her nose. The woman didn't acknowledge the men but instead walked to the far side of the courtyard. Dave looked at the minister and shrugged his shoulders.

Burke said softly, "Nurse Becky told me that she's not a happy woman. I stopped by to introduce myself the other day, and she made it clear that because she doesn't believe in God she wants nothing to do with me."

"Clarity in communication is good," Dave said with a smile.

Burke smirked. "No one would accuse her of being ambiguous. Becky said she won't let anyone visit her. Her adult children have come to see her at the hospital, but she won't even see them."

Hearing this detail triggered a thought, so Dave decided to share something he believed might be helpful to his friend. "I'd like to share something with you that I think might be relevant to your situation with your father. Is that okay?"

"You've never steered me wrong."

"Have I ever explained to you my philosophy on why the people who challenge us or hurt us are in our lives?"

"I have my own ideas, but I'd love to hear yours."

"Well, I'll give you my take on it, for what it's worth." Dave took a deep breath and gathered his thoughts. Then he said, "The people in our lives—our friends, family members, coworkers, employees, and employers—serve as mirrors to us. They reflect back to us where we need growth and healing. And they will continue to do this until we either heal the part of us that they're showing us or they grow in such a way that they are no longer a match for us. If they grow and move on, someone else is sure to fill their place until we don't need it anymore."

Burke thought about it. "I'm pretty sure I know the concept, but I'm not clear on why you're sharing it with me now. Please continue."

Dave thought about the proper terminology to use with his religious friend. "Let me say it a different way," he finally said. "I don't think our relationships exist without divine influence. I believe every person helps every other person in his or her life to grow, to learn, and to heal."

The minister nodded, waiting for more.

"It all starts with our families, right? Those are the people God set up for us in order that we have particular childhood experiences that will set us on the path He chose for us. Would you agree?"

"Most definitely," said Burke.

"I don't believe every parent-child relationship is what we might consider healthy," Dave continued, "but I do believe that every parent-child relationship is such that it sets us on a path to learn very valuable lessons, information we will know for the rest of our lives and for all eternity. Are you still with me?"

"Very much so. Continue."

"Well, some of our familial relationships are painful, so they require us to heal. From the healing of our pain come the lessons God intends for us to learn. If we separate from those painful family relationships before we heal, who do you think we attract into our lives to help us heal that pain?"

"Other people."

"Exactly: friends, coworkers, employers, business partners, lovers, spouses. We attract friends, for instance, who are like energetic puzzle pieces that fit perfectly with our own energetic puzzle pieces. If I'm needy, I'll attract someone who likes to be needed. If I'm weak, I'll attract someone who likes being the strong person in a relationship. If I'm a caretaker, I will attract someone who needs to be cared for. If I'm not good at having fun, I'll attract a friend who teaches me to play."

"Thinking of my friends over the years, this notion has definitely played out in my life," said Father Burke.

"Not every family member or friend is going to fit into this scenario, but most will have something to either teach us, even if just by example, or to be taught by us. But the most challenging relationships, I've found, are some of the most important."

"Can you give me an example from your own life?" asked the minister.

"I can. When I was a teenager, I ran my own odd job business. I would mow lawns, wash windows, clean leaf gutters, all types of basic handyman work. I made pretty good money at it, too, at least for my age. My father always struggled financially, so my success mirrored to him what he was not able to accomplish. The result was that he felt threatened by my financial success.

"One day I bought a new car with the money I had saved from my hard work. It was a used car, but it was new to me. It was nice. It was a black Chevy El Camino SS, which was sort of a car with a pickup truck bed. It had five-spoke SS wheels, a bench seat so my girl could cuddle up to me, a v-eight engine with aluminum heads, and four on the floor.

"When I brought my new car home from the dealership to show my family, it was more than obvious that my father was jealous. He wouldn't even look at it when the rest of my family came outside to check it out. After that day, he got more and more competitive with me, and let me just say that it is really odd to have your own father being competitive with you instead of supportive and happy for your successes in life."

"I can only imagine," said Burke.

The woman with the oxygen tank walked slowly by the men again on her way back toward the hospital doorway. Again, she didn't look at them. Dave waited for her to leave before finishing his story. When the automatic doors opened and she stepped through with her tank, he continued.

"Well, my father died when I was still young, so I was unable to heal that part of our relationship. Consequently, years later, someone new came into my life to fill his place. I didn't know it then, but this person showed up to help me heal the damage caused by my father's inability to be proud of my successes."

"Do you know what that damage was?" asked the minister.

"I do now. I didn't then. I knew subconsciously that my father showed me love when I failed, when I was sick, or when I was in turmoil. Yet he withheld his love when I was successful financially, when I won an award at school, or when I excelled in sports. Worse than with-holding his love, he actually got mean when he learned about my successes. He would give me more chores, criticize what I did, and not allow me to do things I wanted, like go to a party I wanted to attend on Saturday night.

"The damage in response to his behavior was that I unconsciously withheld myself from succeeding anymore. I pulled myself back from achieving many things I could have in my life. In a sense, I diminished myself in order to make my father feel better about himself."

"Sadly, that makes sense," said the minister. "I've seen that same response from several children I've counseled."

"So years after my father passed, I made a new friend. We had a lot in common. We had a lot of fun together. And he became very dear to both Margie and me. But guess what?"

"He got competitive with you?"

"Yup. In less than a year, I learned he was the type of person who was *very* competitive. He liked to surround himself with people who were less successful than him so that he could be the most successful person among his friends. This made him feel better about himself. I believe he was attracted to me because I had this automatic trigger inside to shrink in order to make others feel superior to me, which was something I learned to do because of my father.

"About a year into our friendship, he became more and more competitive with me. He could never feel happy for my career successes, yet he always expected me to be happy for his, and, of course, I was genuinely happy for his achievements in life. Sadly, for me at least, this was a constant thorn in our relationship. I recognized it and it angered me, but I never confronted him about it."

Father Burke's attention was focused on Dave's story. He sat quietly facing him, waiting to hear what happened next.

Dave continued. "I have always been proactive about my personal growth, so I went to my therapist one day with the intention of dealing with this issue. This was twelve years into my relationship with this guy. I was aware of my friend's competitiveness toward me, but I wasn't yet aware of the similarity between my father's behavior and his. I had never made the connection until that day.

"I went into meditation with the therapist, which is something we did in every session. My awareness heightened and my understanding of this friendship became clear. I had a big-picture view of everything that was going on between us. I also recognized that my friend was providing me with an opportunity to heal the wound that I wasn't able to heal with my dad."

Dave repositioned his body and put his hand on Burke's shoulder. "What this bird's-eye view from my meditation provided me was the ability to see my father's behavior and my friend's behavior for what it really was. Their reaction to what I was doing was related to their own demons.

"It wasn't that they didn't love me. It was that they both had past wounds of their own that triggered them to feel poorly about themselves when other people around them succeeded, even if those other people were family members or friends. You see, Father, I learned that it was never about how they felt about me. It was always about how they felt about themselves. And that paradigm shift made all the difference for me."

Burke's eyes got misty. "That was a powerful recognition," he said.

Dave went on. "Like a bolt of awareness, I recognized how my father's energy and my friend's energy were like puzzle pieces that fit perfectly with my own energetic puzzle. I got home from that therapy session and coincidentally—divine coincidence—my wife, Margie, was

173

talking to this very friend on the phone. He was saying something indicating to her that he was being competitive with me and it was upsetting her because she knew how much it hurt me when he did that.

"I got in from my incredible therapy session right as she hung up the phone feeling angry at him. She told me what he said and it had absolutely no emotional effect on me. I knew in that moment that whatever hold my friend's energy had on me prior to that day had released because of my new awareness. My perception had shifted. The torment was finally over."

"Wow! What was that like?" asked Burke.

"I knew in that moment that our relationship would change because a transformation had occurred. I still loved my friend. I just knew that the energetic cords that held us together for twelve years had broken. I no longer needed someone I loved to be so fiercely competitive with me. I no longer needed to be in a relationship that was as one-sided as ours, with me supporting him but not the other way around.

"I also knew what I felt wasn't imaginary. It was real. And I knew my friend felt it, too. Without any word between us—no kind words and no harsh words—we naturally drifted apart after that day. We saw each other once or twice a year. I still felt love for him. I'm sure he felt the same. I even grieved the loss of the friendship as I had known it. However, after that day, I moved forward in my life a changed man."

The automatic doors to the hospital opened, and a technician walked into the courtyard. He was looking around the courtyard for someone. Father Burke spoke up. "Looking for a woman with a tank in tow?"

"Yes. Seen her?"

"She was here a few minutes ago. I saw her take a left through the doors."

"Thanks, Father. She keeps walking off before her treatment. I know where she went."

The technician hurried out the door and down the hallway. Father Burke turned his attention back to Dave. "That's quite a story. If you don't mind sharing, how did this transformation affect your life?"

"The effect was significant. My career and finances flourished after that day. I realized how many ways I had been holding back my own success in order not to upset someone I loved. I had not done so consciously. Nonetheless, once I was free from my unconscious response to their conditional love, I took off like a rocket in many different areas of my life."

"That's a great example of how our relationships can hold us back," Burke commented.

"Especially those that are troublesome, Father. That's why I've told you my story, if only as a reminder to you. Your relationship with your father has likely affected you in one way or another throughout your entire life. In your case, it was your lack of a relationship with him that impacted you. Some people affect us without even being present."

Two black butterflies with a hint of blue in their wings flew in front of the men, appearing to be playing. One landed, and the other flew off. When that one landed, the other flew toward it. Eventually they both flew side by side until they landed on a fence surrounding the courtyard.

Burke looked at Dave. "The way you describe your experience, it's clear you do not see yourself as a victim in either of these cases. I would concur with that. Everyone has these troublesome relationships in their lives, right? No one is excluded. Instead of being victimized by them, if we view our challenging relationships as being there to teach us something God wants us to know, we can learn our lessons faster. Is that your take on it?"

"For sure," said Dave, nodding. "We all have our issues. Our family members and friends have their stuff, and we have our stuff. What

I find especially healing in my own life is to try to understand what their stuff is. I believe if we can recognize why they might be thinking or saying the things they do or acting the way they do, we can resolve the issues that plague us, or at least remove the emotional charges we feel around them. This leads to detachment, which is a giant leap forward from being emotionally captured and controlled by our emotional stuff."

Father Burke was excited that Dave had mentioned the concept. "In my own counseling work in the Episcopal church and also here at the hospital, I have witnessed this in action. When people are able to see why the other people are acting the way they are, they almost always realize it has nothing to do with them. Instead, there's usually something going on with the other person at home, school, or work that is behind the hurtful words or actions. Often one person is merely misinterpreting the other. That happens a lot. When people are able to stop taking things personally, it removes that emotional charge you mentioned, which helps everyone see with more clarity."

"When I taught at the college, Father, I would teach my students that perspective is thought and thought is energy—creative energy. Creative energy coupled with emotion is a very powerful force.

"If our perspective is such that we take other people's words or actions personally, that powerful force, basically our feelings about their words or actions, can turn our lives upside down. Therefore, giving ourselves distance in order to see another person's perspective can save us a lot of misery."

The minister took a deep breath and seemed to relax. "I really appreciate you reminding me of that insight and sharing your personal story with me. I'm going to keep that in mind when I go to visit my father at the shelter. I'm going to look for the lesson if I can recognize it. And I'm going to try to understand his perspective on why he walked away from his responsibility to raise me. Perhaps the stories I've been telling myself my whole life are not accurate."

"Amen, Father."

The two men sat quietly together in the courtyard garden. After five minutes had passed, Paula walked into the courtyard looking for them. "Hey Father. Don't mean to interrupt your discussion out here, but someone else has requested last rites. It's been one of those days."

Dave asked, "Do they still call it last rites?"

"That was a Catholic phrase from the past. I think most Christians call it *ministration to the sick* or *ministry with the sick*. I usually call it *praying with the sick*. What we don't say is *ministry to the dying* because you just never know. I've prayed with people who thought they were dying only to see them walk out of the hospital two weeks later and live long lives."

Dave nodded with a smile.

The minister stood up and grabbed Dave's hand, looking him in the eyes. "I'll get the details from you later about meeting my father. I'm scared, but I'm grateful. You're a good friend for investigating his whereabouts for me," he said, patting his friend's hand. Then he and Paula walked back through the doors into the hospital while Dave stayed in the courtyard.

Dave used the moment to visualize a healing meeting between Jonathan Burke and his father, George.

CHAPTER TWENTY-FOUR:
THE MIGHTY FEMININE

IT'S GOING TO cost more to fix it than the car is worth? It's not going to pass inspection? It's time to trade it in? That's what he said?" asked Robby.

Mary nodded. "The mechanic's exact words."

Robby kicked his empty plastic trashcan across his office and fell into his chair. "Such lousy timing," he said.

Mary walked up behind him, kissed him on the head, and caressed the back of his neck. "We're doing fine. There's the income I'm earning at Jankowitz, and we still have money in the bank from your contract with Dale. That's why clients pay so much up front. If something happens, like it did to Dale, you get compensated because it takes so long to get another client. Only this time, you're going to be your own client."

Robby agonized at the idea of spending money. It was difficult for him to feel confident that everything was going to work out. He wished he could be like Mary, but optimism didn't come as naturally to him.

"What if I don't get a publishing contract? What will happen to us then?"

"Don't forget, Robby, I'm earning more from my drawings at work now. We'll get by, we really will. Plus, you have to believe. You have to stop your negative thinking. You know how harmful that is."

Mary always knew how to zero in on what Robby needed to hear. The last thing he wanted was to create what he feared by thinking pessimistically. He took a deep breath and tried to surrender to the present moment. "I know. I know. You're right. What choice do we have, really? The old wagon's not going to pass inspection. On the other hand, maybe we could get by with just one car for a while."

"Robby, if you drive me to work and pick me up every day, that's two hours of driving each day when you could be writing your book. In addition to which I won't have a car to run errands during my lunch breaks. That means you'll have to go to the bank, grocery store, health food store, post office, and anywhere else I would normally go. That's another hour a day that you could be writing. In a five-day work-week, that's fifteen hours a week you'll be driving around instead of writing—all because you have a stronger belief in failure than success."

Robby thought about it for a moment and looked up at Mary who was still standing behind him caressing his neck. "You have a better handle on the power of our thoughts than I do. You're right. Fifteen hours a week is a lot of time to forfeit in order to save a few hundred dollars a month. Geez, that's like sixty hours a month." He hesitated in thought and then added, "Okay, but you're in charge when we go to the dealership. I hate dealing with car salesmen, and your father taught you all their secrets. So I'm just coming along to support you, okay?"

Mary lifted her hand in the air and he high-fived it.

"Leave in five minutes?" she asked.

"I'm thrilled," he said sarcastically.

Robby really despised buying cars. The tension, the manipulation, and the negotiation strategies turned his stomach. He was glad Mary wasn't intimidated by it.

On the ride to the dealership, she instructed Robby on what would happen. "The salesman is going to want to talk to you. No matter how far we think we've come in gender equality, most male contractors, real estate agents, and salespeople in almost every industry still automatically look at the husband when a decision needs to be made. Whatever you do, don't get involved in the negotiation. Just keep telling them that it's my car, my decision."

"Got it. Are we financing it in your name this time?"

"Hell no! Your credit is better, so we'll get a better rate. But we won't spring that on them until the very end. They'll use any excuse to increase the finance rate."

"What are all these papers you brought?" he asked her.

Pointing to each one, she told him, "That's the newspaper advertisement they now have in the *Worcester Telegram*. It's for a cheaper model, but it gives me a price point to shoot for. Some of these car ads will show a low price on a model that they don't even have in stock."

She then pointed to another sheet of paper. "That there is the Kelley Blue Book 'fair market price' for the year, model, and options I want. It tells me the invoice price that the dealership paid for the car. With incentives, the dealership can often go under that price. It tells me what the fair market range is within about a thousand dollars. It also tells me the MSRP, which is the typical sticker price for new cars, or the CPO, which is the typical sticker price for used cars."

"How much do you want to pay?"

"As close to invoice—or better, as much *under* the invoice price— as I can get them. I don't mind the dealership making a few hundred dollars over the invoice price, unless the manufacturer has given the dealership incentives this month. If those exist, we can get under the invoice price while the dealership still makes money."

"Wait! Are you talking about the sticker price?"

"No, the sticker price is what's on the window. Pay no attention to that. The invoice price is what the dealership paid for the vehicle, which I know from the Kelly Blue Book. I only talk invoice price, how much I will pay under or over what the dealership paid."

"How do you know if incentives exist?"

"You can sometimes tell by the newspaper ad. Or you can tell by the Kelly Blue Book 'fair market range.' If the 'fair market range' is below what they say the invoice price is, that's an indication that there are incentives. Otherwise, you hope the salesman will tell you—but that often requires a lot of negotiation or luck."

"And what about a finance rate?"

"The newspaper shows me that the dealership can go as low as two point nine percent on the vehicle I want. But I'll probably have to ask for less in order to get it. The secret is to always ask for much less than you're willing to spend in order to eventually land where you want because they are going to do the opposite. This is true for both the price and the finance rate."

Robby was proud of his wife. Her father had taught her well. He had been the sales manager for a dealership the last several years of his life, so he knew all the tricks of the trade. He had wanted his only child to know them, too. Her dad always told her, "If you know how to negotiate, it's a skill you will use your entire life."

They pulled into the Toyota dealership, shut off the wagon, and it backfired with a bang. The couple broke out laughing. Per Mary's instructions, they waited a few minutes so that anyone who heard the backfire wouldn't see them get out of the car.

"We don't want them to think we're desperate to buy," Mary told Robby.

When it seemed like nobody was looking, they got out and looked at the RAV4 model SUV Mary had decided to buy.

Mary found the model and color she liked, and a car salesman came up to them. "You need any help?" he asked.

"No, we're already working with another salesperson," said Mary.

"Which one? Can I get him or her for you?"

"They already know we're out here."

Mary didn't like lying, but it was part of the car-buying game. Her daddy had taught her to think of it like a game, not a lie, and definitely not a fight. "It's a game of skills," he told her, "just like chess or poker. Keep your emotions out of it. Emotions have no place in negotiations. If you think of it as a game, you can keep it fun and focus on winning."

Now that Mary had found the car she was interested in buying, she was searching for the right salesperson. Robby followed her as she walked around the dealership. "What are you looking for?" he asked.

"I'm just looking at the salespeople. I'm using my intuition to choose the right one."

"Did your father teach you that?"

"No, my daddy didn't know about intuition. I learned that from Caroline and your father."

"My father? When?"

"You know that we have lunch now and then."

"Yeah, but I didn't know you talked about stuff like intuition with him."

"We talk about all sorts of things." She paused. "Okay, he's the one." She pointed to a nice-looking man sitting at his sales desk. He was about six-foot-two with blond hair cut very short. He looked like he might have played football or wrestled in school.

"Why him?" Robby asked.

"He's got kind eyes. I saw him talking with that woman over there. He was gentle, and he held the door open for her. But more importantly, my intuition tells me he's the one."

"When you say *intuition*, what does that mean exactly?"

"To me it means a gut feeling. When I look at that salesman, I feel good. When that other salesman approached us outside, I felt the opposite—uneasy, almost nervous."

Mary approached the salesman whose name was Chris. She told him she'd like to take a car for a test drive, and she gave him the inventory number that she had taken from a sticker on the vehicle's windshield. He looked it up on his computer and left to get the keys and a dealer's plate.

After the test drive, Mary sat down with Chris at his desk. Robby sat next to her. Chris looked at Robby. "How much a month do you want to spend?"

"Ask Mary. This is her car," Robby told him.

"Sorry. Mary, how much a month do you want to spend?"

"I'm going to save you some time, Chris. I only want to talk invoice, not monthly payments. Truthfully, I don't want to pay anything monthly."

Robby chuckled. He always liked his wife's humor.

"Do you have a car you're trading in?" asked Chris. He made sure to look right at Mary, only glancing at Robby every now and then.

"No."

Robby knew what she was doing. She had told him earlier that in order to talk car price only and not get confused by the different numbers, she would negotiate a price on the car she was buying before mentioning she had a car to trade.

Mary pulled out the Kelley Blue Book sheet she had printed from the internet. "This is your invoice price," she told Chris. "I see that the 'fair market price' is lower than the invoice price, so that tells me there are manufacturer incentives. What incentives does the manufacturer give the dealership on this model?"

"My goodness, you came prepared. I'll have to check with the sales manager," said Chris, and he walked away.

Once Chris was gone, Mary told Robby, "When I get up to walk out, follow me without any questions, okay?"

"Sure thing, honey. You're the master."

Chris came back. "There aren't any incentives on that model. I'm sorry. It's a popular car, so we don't see incentives very often on that model."

Mary sat up straight in her chair. She wasn't sure whether or not to believe Chris, but she was suspicious. "Chris, based on an advertisement you have in the newspaper and the Kelley Blue Book, there must be some incentives from the manufacturer. But all that matters is what I pay for the vehicle, so I'll overlook that for now. What's the percentage rate for financing?" she asked.

"I can get you seven point nine percent." Chris pointed to a sign on the wall that read: Today's finance rate 7.9 percent.

Mary gave Chris an irritated look. "I don't have a lot of time, Chris. I don't blame you, however, for doing what you have to do. I know your sales manager has certain expectations of you. But how long have you been selling cars here?"

"Twenty-five years."

"Good. That will save us both time. Let's do this a little differently. I'll tell you how to get me into that car today. Sell me the car I just drove for three hundred under invoice at one point nine percent financing and I'll buy it now. If not, give me your best deal and I'll go see what the Toyota dealership in Framingham will offer me. I don't mind driving forty-five minutes to save money."

Chris looked at her, then he looked at Robby. Robby shrugged his shoulders and smiled. "I'll see what I can do," he said. He went back into the sales manager's office.

"Get ready to start walking out," she told Robby.

He nodded.

Chris came back. "Okay, I think we have a pretty good deal for you. Fifteen hundred dollars over invoice, but that doesn't include the six-hundred-dollar destination fee that you have to pay no matter what. I can go as low as four point nine percent on financing."

Mary gathered her papers and purse and stood up. Robby followed suit. She put her hand out to shake Chris's and said, "Thank you for your time, Chris. It was really nice to meet you." After Chris shook her hand, she headed for the door.

Chris looked surprised that she was leaving and chased after her. "Wait! Let me talk to the finance guy. Maybe he can figure out a way to get you a lower percentage rate. One of the finance guys here is my friend."

"Sure," said Mary, "but we're still way off on the price of the vehicle. I don't see how that's going to help." She stood beside the door with her hand on it like she was ready to push it open. "Chris, I told you I don't have a lot of time. If you can get me three hundred under invoice and one point nine percent financing, I'll sign the papers right now. But you're so far off that I don't see how you're going to do it."

"Please sit back down and give me one more chance. I think I can do better," Chris begged.

Mary opened the door. She spoke in a kind but confident voice. "We're going to wait outside, Chris. I want to be in the sun. We'll wait out here for you, but you know what it's going to take to sell me a car today."

Chris left for about five minutes and came back outside to where they were standing. He showed Mary the paper where he had written his figures. "I talked with my friend in the finance department, and he told me that two point nine is the lowest he can go on that model."

Mary crossed her arms in front of her like she wasn't impressed, but was waiting for his newest vehicle price.

"And we looked up that RAV4 that you drove and noticed it has five hundred miles on it already, which is getting kind of high for a new car. I had to fight for it, but I can give it to you for a hundred dollars under invoice. That's a really good deal, Mary. The sales manager's niece didn't even get that good a deal last week."

"Make it two hundred under invoice, and you have a deal."

Chris looked back toward the sales manager's office and his face turned red. "I can't even go back in there, Mary. That's really the best I can do."

"Well, that's what I was waiting for. You have a deal, Chris. But while we were waiting, we decided that we don't really feel like having to sell our car. I'd like to know, what can you give us for a trade in?"

Mary wasn't expecting any profit from her wagon. She was happy just to get rid of it without having to pay anything, especially since her mechanic had told her the repairs needed would cost more than the car. She was honest about the needed repairs, and the dealership agreed to take the car even though it would likely go to the auction or junkyard.

Mary drove home in her new RAV4 while Robby sat in the passenger's seat praising her on how amazing she was at negotiating with the salesman. "I just have one question, Mary."

"What's that, honey?"

"I don't understand how our intention exercises play into all this."

"Oh, I set the intention on getting a great deal. I even wrote it down and read it out loud several times. As I read it, I visualized it going smoothly and successfully in my mind."

"But it was still a lot of work."

"That's just how the car business works, sweetie. The trick is to integrate our intention practices with the way the real world works. Like your father told me, the work we're doing is magical, not magic. To be honest, I got the deal I wanted a lot faster than I expected. If I hadn't learned what I did about intention from Caroline and your father, we'd probably still be negotiating."

Robby asked, "But with the right intention and belief, could someone walk into the dealership and get a great deal without good negotiation skills?"

"Anything is possible. We have to remember that a great deal is very subjective, Robby. Some people never negotiate. They walk in and pay the sticker price. Others hope to get a few hundred dollars off the sticker price. Regardless, most people go home happy."

"But you got nearly five thousand dollars off the sticker price!" he said loudly.

"People don't know what they don't know, Robby. As long as they go home happy, that's what matters."

"Well, I'm feeling really grateful for your father right now and all that he taught you. I'm also really glad that you learned it so well and have the nerve to apply what you learned."

"Me, too, Robby. Me, too."

"You know, Mary, if you want to drive my pickup truck for a while, I can help break this vehicle in for you."

"Sure," she said with a grin. "And if you want to break in those sneakers you're wearing, I can drop you off and you can walk home from here."

Robby sat in the passenger's seat with a big smirk on his face, appreciating the mighty feminine in all her strength and beauty.

CHAPTER TWENTY-FIVE:
THE DOOM

ROBBY WAS ON the front steps of their condo with his head hung low. *This is it,* he thought to himself. *It's over. Everything the magic mala gave me is now going to unravel. My mojo is gone. The dream is over. My luck has turned.*

Robby closed his eyes as if he was waiting for a meteor to drop on him. He didn't even look up when Mary drove into the driveway. She got out of her new SUV and walked up to him slowly.

She leaned against the stairway railing. "Something wrong, honey?"

"I'm trying not to panic," he told her. "I'm doing my best to avoid going into fear mode, but I don't think I'm doing too well."

Mary climbed the steps and sat next to him.

"You're going to have to say it out loud sometime. What happened?"

"I lost my mala."

Mary was relieved that it wasn't a terrible tragedy like someone's death or serious injury.

"You might still find it. When was the last time you had it?"

"That's the problem. I used it this morning when I went for a walk, then I thought I placed it in my back pocket. The hitch is that I walked like two miles around the reservoir."

"Did you go anywhere else today?"

Robby nodded his head while still staring at his feet. "It was the busiest day of my life. After my walk, I went to the bank, Matt's store, the office supply store, the pharmacy, and Starbucks."

There was a minute of silence. Mary thought about what to do. She had always been good at thinking clearly when other people were panicking.

"Let's look up the phone numbers to all the businesses you visited and then I'll call them while we retrace your steps around the reservoir." Mary walked inside the condo and jumped onto the internet to get the phone numbers. Robby followed, opened the fridge, and pulled out a container of cottage cheese.

"What are you doing?" she asked.

"I'm starving."

She laughed and shook her head back and forth. "You always eat when you're nervous."

After Mary finished writing down the phone numbers, they left the condo in search of the mala beads. Mary's optimism had Robby feeling slightly hopeful.

"There's an awful lot of stuff on the road that got crushed by cars," noticed Robby.

"There's not a lot of traffic today. Try to hold off on the 'We'll never make it' attitude." Mary had her cellphone to her ear. "Hold on, it's ringing . . ." She got through to the bank and waited on hold while they looked around and checked the lost and found. They didn't have it.

"That's okay," she assured her husband. "One down, four to go."

They continued walking down the road, looking carefully in the grass for the mala beads.

"I went down here next," said Robby as he detoured onto a cart road. Mary followed.

"Which side did you walk on?" she asked.

"Down the middle, I guess," he said, sounding frustrated. His efforts to remain hopeful were failing.

"How about we each take a side," she suggested. "I'll stay toward the left, you the right."

Mary called Matt at his store and told him what happened.

"Oh boy, how's Pessimistic Pete taking it?"

"Not so good."

"I'm sorry, but I haven't seen it. I'll look around and call you if the mala shows up. However, I just swept the floors and they're not on the counter, so I don't think they're here."

Mary gave Robby the news. As much as she didn't like seeing him fearful, she made an effort to remain detached from his mood. She knew that losing his mala wasn't the worst thing in the world. Instead, she focused on the beauty of nature while she walked down the cart road. She admired the trees, the wildflowers, and the water. She felt so connected to the landscape and wildlife that she wondered why she didn't take this walk herself more often.

Robby's nervous pace led him to walk far ahead of his wife.

She called the next place on her list. "I'm sorry, ma'am. There's nothing like that in the lost and found," said the manager at the office supply store. Mary was glad she didn't have to deliver the news to Robby. He was too far in front of her. She was about to make the next phone call when she looked up to see Robby sitting on a fallen tree. He was clearly upset by something. She caught up to him and asked, "Why did you stop searching?"

"This is where I turned around. I walked back the same way we came."

"Oh, I see. Well, I still have two more places to call. But tell me, honey, why is this upsetting you so much? Tell me what you're feeling."

"I'm feeling sadness, fear . . . doom."

"Doom? Why doom?"

"I felt safe with that mala. I felt I could accomplish anything with it. It was my good luck charm. What am I supposed to do now? I'm about to go to New York with Matt, and I wanted it with me.

She stood in front of him and lifted his chin so he'd look at her. "We can get you a new mala, Robby. We have a lot of nice ones at the jewelry store. We can go tonight."

"What if I don't have the same results with another mala? There was something special about that one, magical. Everything was going so well for us. Why did this have to happen now?"

Mary knew her husband well. She knew that when he was upset about something, he needed time to process all the fearful thoughts that were consuming him. Nothing she could say at this point would help until he worked it out himself. She called the pharmacy, hoping they might have some good news to put an end to all this.

"I'm sorry, we haven't found anything today," the young girl who answered the phone told Mary.

Mary shook her head so Robby knew it was a no. She immediately dialed Starbucks.

"We have something that kind of looks like that here," the man said. "It's a necklace with lots of beads. I guess they're blue. Can you come by today?"

"Yes, we'll come right down."

"Just ask for Michael. I'll be here until eight o'clock tonight."

Mary relayed the message to Robby. "I'm not sure it's your mala, honey. But it's worth going down there. He wasn't sure it was blue. I'd say your mala is clearly blue, so let's just wait and see."

Robby and Mary jumped in the RAV4, and she drove them to Starbucks. They arrived in fifteen minutes. They ran in and asked for Michael. He pulled out a mala, but the beads weren't lapis; they were hematite. Robby's last bit of hope fizzled.

Mary didn't try to encourage him on the drive back to the condo. She knew it would be fruitless. When they arrived home, he jumped out of the SUV before she had a chance to shut off the engine. "I'm going to take a nap," he told her before he slammed the SUV door.

Robby went inside, and Mary called Caroline while sitting in the car. She explained the situation.

"I can understand. It's because it was his first mala," Caroline told Mary. "He's come a long way since finding it. He's probably scared about the future, and I think he's probably grieving the loss as well."

"So how do I help him? You're the teacher. What advice would you give one of your students?"

Caroline sighed and thought about it. "It's believed that when your mala beads break, it's time for a new one. The energy of the beads is no longer compatible with the energy of the owner. It's probably the same when you lose it. Aside from that, I think he should talk to Matt. He speaks Robby's language. I'll send him over tomorrow morning."

Mary was glad Robby had gone for a nap. She decided to take another walk around the reservoir. She probably wouldn't find the missing mala, but the nature walk would help raise her energy now that Robby's mood had bummed her out a little.

CHAPTER TWENTY-SIX:
THE RELEASE

FATHER BURKE parked in front of the shelter, his hands trembling on the steering wheel. He squeezed his hands together, hoping to stop them. It didn't help, so he placed them in his pockets.

He entered the shelter and walked into the dining hall, where Dave had arranged for him and George to meet. The dining hall was empty, being mid-morning, except for a couple of people who were cleaning. There were several round tables, each with six chairs .

Burke had wondered how he would recognize the father he'd never seen, yet he knew him the second he laid eyes on him. George was seated alone at one of the tables; nevertheless, he could have picked him out of a busy crowd. It was like looking at himself in twenty years.

Every step he took toward the man, his heart beat faster. He thought about turning around and leaving, but he knew he'd always regret it. After a few more steps, he realized it was too late to turn back. "George?" he asked as he walked up to the man. He noticed his father's hands were shaking, too.

George stood up and held his hand out. Burke stared at it for a few seconds, thinking to himself, *This is really happening. After sixty-six years, I'm finally meeting my father.* He shook George's hand. There was an awkward quietness that seemed to last forever. After a few moments, Father Burke broke the silence. "Well, I guess I was the one who asked to meet you, so I might as well begin. You know, I knew for years what I would say to you if I ever saw you, but suddenly it all feels wrong. You look, well . . . old."

The two men laughed loudly.

"My goodness, you haven't changed a bit, Jonathan," his father said, chuckling.

His comment confused the minister. "What do you mean? How would you know anything about me?"

"Son—" Suddenly George got scared. "I'm sorry. I just call young people that."

"No, it's fine. You may call me son." Burke's eyes welled up with tears as the simple meaning of what he was saying sunk in.

"Oh, thank you." George's eyes also got watery. "The truth is that I watched you grow up, although always from a distance. Your grandparents, I mean, your parents, would let me know if you were ever going to be anywhere that I could see you. I watched you at the park and the Boys Club when you were little. I saw you play baseball from the time you were seven right up through high school, at least whenever you played somewhere I could reach by walking." He chuckled. "I might have lived to this old age because you had me walking all over the city."

Burke tried to swallow his tears, but they just kept coming. He was confused.

"Please sit down, Jonathan," George requested.

Burke sat down on the chair next to the stranger who was his father. "If you attended those events, why didn't you ever let me know? I would have liked to know. I was under the impression you didn't care, that you didn't love me."

George looked down at the ground, unable to look his son in the eyes. "All right, since we're doing this, I assume you want the truth, right?"

"The truth would be nice, yeah," said the minister.

George talked slowly. "Okay, the truth. The truth is that I was sleeping in a cardboard box. I had no money. Strangers told me I smelled." George choked up but quickly contained his emotions. He continued. "I was drunk most of the time, and I didn't want to embarrass you. I didn't want you to know who your dad really was. I preferred you to think I was dead than to know the truth. I didn't want you growing up thinking you might be anything like me."

Father Burke looked around the room. His breathing was heavy. He wasn't sure if he wanted to yell at his father or hug him.

"I was weak," continued George. "I've been weak most of my life. My father even told me I was weak when I was a boy. Your mother was the opposite. She was brave and bright-eyed. She was smart. She knew how to keep me sober. But I was codependent. When she died, I didn't know how to deal with my grief. I didn't know how to deal with life. And I certainly didn't know how to raise a little boy."

George had to catch his breath before he picked up again. "She was always the breadwinner. I was a phony. We both pretended I was more than I was. When she died giving birth to you, I brought you to her parents. That was the smartest thing I ever did aside from marrying your mother. I knew it was right. They knew it. Everybody who knew me knew it."

They sat for a moment without talking. When Burke's anxiety subsided, he moved his chair closer to his father to say what he needed to say.

"I always thought you gave me away because she died giving birth to me. I thought you blamed me. I was sure you didn't love me, even though Mom's parents said otherwise. I figured they had to say that. I couldn't invent one logical reason why any father would do what you did. As I got older, people told me you were homeless. They told me you drank. I didn't care. All I ever wanted from you was love."

He gathered himself before saying more. "I was so angry with you . . . and I hated the way that anger made me feel. I hated myself for hating you. When I got older, maybe twenty years ago, I assumed you were dead. I was driving down Interstate 295 and knew I had to release my anger. I had to forgive you. Not for you as much as for myself. I needed to release that burden of hating you. I did not know where you were buried, so I just drove to the nearest cemetery I could find. I pulled in and got out of my car in front of a large statue of Saint Francis of Assisi. I fell to my knees, and I talked to the statue like I was talking to you. Right there, as I kneeled on the ground, I forgave you. I truly forgave you in my heart. All my old hatred and anger was released in that moment. And now here you are in front of me, and I still feel no anger at you. I'm sixty-six years old, and I still only need you to love me."

Father Burke burst out sobbing. The reunited father and son held one another as they each trembled after their cathartic confessions. For nearly thirty minutes, they held one another for the first time since Jonathan was born more than six decades earlier.

When they were both exhausted from all the emotion, George held his son's hands and said, "I know I have a strange way of showing it, but I never blamed you for what happened to your mom. I have always loved you. That's why I watched you grow up every opportunity I could."

George and Jonathan spent a couple of hours together. They caught up on each other's lives, as best they could, and they arranged to see one another the following week so the minister could show his father the chapel where he worked. They departed that day as completely different men than the two who had entered the shelter just a few hours earlier.

When Father Burke got back into his car, he was numb from the release and purging that had just occurred. It took him ten minutes before he was ready to turn the ignition key. As he drove away, he thought to himself, *Dave was right. The stories I invented as a boy were all wrong. Thank you, God and Jesus, for giving me the opportunity to learn the truth before one of us died.*

Burke drove by an ice cream shop and pulled over to get himself a cone. He felt like a boy again, so it seemed appropriate. He licked his ice cream cone, grateful for what had just occurred and in awe at the complexities of life about which he was still learning.

A little boy appeared in front of the minister, pointing at him. Father Burke didn't understand what he wanted, so the boy walked closer, now pointing at his chest. Burke looked down to see that he had dripped ice cream onto his shirt. The boy then held his own ice cream cone above his shirt and let it drip all over it. He looked up at the minister with a mischievous grin. Burke then mimicked the boy, covering his own shirt with more drips of ice cream. The boy screamed in enthusiasm and ran back toward his parents. The minister then finished his cone, got back in his car, and drove home with a shirt covered in ice cream and a second chance at having the boyhood he had always wanted.

CHAPTER TWENTY-SEVEN:

THE PARADIGM SHIFT

MATT WALKED INTO Robby and Mary's home about eight thirty in the morning. Mary was standing at the kitchen island placing flowers that she'd cut from the garden in a vase. Robby was on the living room sofa watching the morning news on television.

Matt walked over to the TV and shut it off, then stood in front of it, giving Robby a look of pity. "Hey, it's the Incredible Sulk. What are you doing? Are you nuts?" Matt said loudly without saying hello. "First you lose your mala, and then you sit around watching the news? Do you know what the news does to you?"

Robby sat upright, annoyed by the interruption. "What's wrong with the news?" he asked.

"What's wrong with the news? Let's see. First, there's a fire that destroyed some family's home and all their belongings. Oh, and then there's that older couple who were found dead in their home. Foul play is suspected. Wait, there's more. A tornado wiped out an entire community in the Midwest. Eight people were killed, including two children. And in case you weren't feeling scared yet, an escaped convict is on the loose and is believed to have been spotted in your area. By the way, he's armed and dangerous."

Mary stopped what she was doing to watch the display Matt was putting on for her husband's benefit. She knew Matt was purposely being patronizing with Robby because that was the only thing he ever responded to when he was in this state of mind. She knew that Matt's intentions were heartfelt, so she sat down on a stool to watch, one hand over her mouth to conceal her amusement with it all.

"And don't change the channel because after the commercial break we'll tell you why half the food in your refrigerator is dangerous and might kill you and why killer bees and plague-infested mosquitos could obliterate you or your loved ones at any moment."

Robby laughed even though he knew Matt was making a point at his expense.

"How do you feel after you've watched the news, Robby? On a scale from one, being scared, to ten, being happy, does the news usually leave you feeling happy about life or SCARED OUT OF YOUR FRIGGING MIND?"

"You're right. I guess I'm usually feeling a lot more fearful after I shut off the news."

"Most people do. And do you know what fear does to your energy? It lowers it. It lowers your energy to the point where it weakens your immune system. Studies have proven it. That means fear makes you more susceptible to getting sick. And I think you know, but I'll still ask, what happens to our thoughts when our energy is low?"

"I'll guess we tend to think negatively?"

"That's right. Caroline calls it *stinking thinking*. And what does stinking thinking attract to you?"

"Bad luck, I imagine," said Robby.

"You got it, my friend. So you lose your mala and your first instinct is to turn on the news?"

"No. My first instinct was to take a nap," Robby admitted.

Matt held back his laughter. He walked over to the sofa and sat beside his friend. "I'm serious, man," he said. "Your power of manifestation is dependent upon what you put into your mind. Let me rephrase that. Your day, your week, and your year are direct reflections of what you pour into your mind.

"If you want a crappy life, watch, listen, or even read the news all day long. It will fill you with so much anxiety that you'll be worried about all sorts of things that will probably never happen.

"It's the same concept as talking incessantly about all the bad things people have done to you in your life. Talk about mean things people have said to you. Talk about the wrongs that were never righted. Talk about all the bad luck you've had with your car or house or health. Talk about it with your friends. Talk about it with your family. Talk about it with the girl at the checkout line at the grocery store. And then talk about it some more with anyone else who will listen."

Matt looked at Mary sitting on a stool in the kitchen. "Can you think of anyone who does that, Mary?"

"Ahh, Stan Barone comes to mind."

"Bingo!" Matt slapped Robby on the leg and smiled. "Look, man, even when you kid around saying crap like 'With my luck, that tornado will come right toward me' or 'The way my health is headed, I'll be dead by Christmas,' you're reinforcing an affirmation and sending the Universe a message that this is what you want in your life—or want more of in your life.

"Regardless of what you're asking the Universe to send you when you talk like that, what you're also doing is depressing your mood, lowering your mental and physical energy, and suppressing your immune system's ability to keep you healthy. And that will lead you to make poor decisions, say things that will only lead to trouble, and snowball your day into chaos, drama, and hell.

"Is that what you want in your life, Noodlenoggin?"

"Definitely not," said Robby. "But how do I stay informed if I don't watch it on TV, listen to it on the radio, or read it in a newspaper?"

Matt leaned over and grabbed a newspaper off the coffee table. He looked at the headlines and chuckled. "It's kind of funny when I think back to when I stopped paying attention to the news. It feels like giving up coffee or chocolate, right? Anything that has been in our lives for years seems necessary. The truth, however, is that you can get along in life just fine without the news. I haven't seen, heard, or read the news in years. Have you even noticed?"

Robby was surprised. "No, I didn't know that. You always seem to be aware of current events. How do you find out if something really bad happens, like a terrorist attack?"

"Naturally I'm going to hear about it from other people. You can't avoid it—nor would I want to. I don't want to be isolated from what's going on in the world. That's not the point. The point is not to fill my mind with negativity, sad news, and fearful messages that aren't necessary.

"Robby, I can't change what happened to the guy who got killed by his drug dealer, the houses that were destroyed in a natural disaster, or whatever fearful events happened on Wall Street on any given day. But I can positively affect the world by keeping my energy up and creating positive change because of it."

Matt walked over to the kitchen sink. He grabbed a dishcloth and soaked it with water. Then he filled up a bowl with water and brought it over to Robby. "Here, hold the bowl, man." Robby held the bowl of water, and Matt held the dishcloth over it. He slowly squeezed it so a drop of water fell into the bowl. "What's this?" Matt asked.

"The ripple effect?"

"That's right. If you understand the concept of the ripple effect and how each and every one of us affects the world by what we think, say, and do, then you understand why I am so passionate about this. What do you think happens if I go to work in a bad mood?"

"You start calling people names like Skidmark and Dufus?"

Mary's giggle echoed from the kitchen.

"No, Motormouth. What happens is that I treat my customers poorly. That discourages them from buying anything and might keep them from ever coming into my store again. They might even tell other people about what a jerk I am, which will discourage them from coming into my store, too.

"Worse than hurting my business success, however, is how I negatively affect our community. When people come into my store, they are almost always happy to be there. They get excited about what I sell and about seeing a baseball or hockey stick signed by someone famous. If I'm grumpy and affect their joy with my personal misery, they take that into our community with them. Now they are in a bad mood, too, because of me, and they negatively affect their employees, coworkers, customers, or the taxicab driver. Some of those people might fly across the world to another country, and now my misery has affected people across the world."

"Instead," Robby chimed in, "you do the opposite. Anytime I've been in your store, I see you improving people's moods. You're always laughing and joking with customers. It's infectious."

"Thanks, Robby. My point, really, is that I treat my customers that way on purpose. I do it because I truly feel joy inside of me, and that's because I am conscious about how I fill my mind."

Matt scratched his head in thought. "You mentioned terrorist attacks. Do you remember Nine-Eleven?"

"Of course," said Robby.

"That happened before I learned what I'm teaching you right now. Do you know what I did that day? I stared at the television most of the day, watching live feeds of the horror that was taking place, including video replays of the planes crashing into the Twin Towers. I didn't just watch it once. I burned that into my brain by watching it over and over for hours. And for months or years after that day, I—along with a lot other Americans who did the same thing—lived in fear of another terrorist attack happening."

Matt pulled some mala beads from his pocket and sat back on the sofa next to Robby. "You know how effective your daily mala practice has been in your life? Well, what is the mala practice, essentially? It's you repeating your positive intention over and over again. Every time you repeat your mantra, you think about what you desire.

"Well, that is what millions of people do whenever there is a school shooting, a sniper on the loose, or a major disaster in the country—except their intentions are negative. They watch the video of a disaster on television over and over, and what happens then? They feel like crap for days or weeks because they have burned fear so far into their brains and bodies that some of those people never feel the same level of joy again.

"How effective do you think it is, Robby, for our society to focus on the fearful events that have taken place to that degree? How many of those people now locked in fear are making the world a better place? How many of them do you think are mentally capable of rushing to help the victims of those tragic events? How many of them do you imagine leave their houses to positively uplift even one other person after watching tragic events on TV for hours, never mind create a ripple effect of love, joy, or kindness in their family, community, country, or the world?"

Robby knew Matt wasn't really expecting an answer. He himself, however, was seeing the world with a new paradigm. He would never really view television news the same way, nor radio, newspapers, books, or content on the internet for that matter.

Matt stood up and began pacing as he talked. "Don't get me wrong, you guys. I don't believe in falsely pretending that bad things don't happen in the world. Nor do I believe that we should forget when they do. I think we should always remember in order to make sure those tragedies don't happen again.

"What I don't think we should do, on the other hand, is focus on them so much that they negatively affect our lives. I don't think we should focus so much on the evil and tragic events in life to the point where we walk around in fear and hopelessness.

"I know people who no longer go out in public places like movie theaters, sporting arenas, and even restaurants because they fear that some nut job might show up shooting people. This is the extreme, Robby, but there are many stages in between, and that's what I'm talking about here. Fear is fear whether you're no longer eating lettuce because of a salmonella outbreak that happened ten years ago or filling your basement with bottled water, sardines, and assault rifles because of an article about terrorism that you read on the internet yesterday."

Matt walked over to the coffee table and picked up the newspaper again. "If you really feel that you can't live without news, at least wean yourself off it. I did that by reading only the newspaper for a while. Try reading just the headlines. Or read only the sections of the paper that you feel necessary, like the national news or world news. Obviously the sports section isn't going to lower your energy . . . unless your favorite team lost the prior night," he said with a smile.

Matt paused to put the dishcloth and bowl back in the sink, so Mary took the opportunity to add something. "Caroline taught me how to increase my energy," she said. "She taught me to get outside to connect with nature. She said that trees, flowers, birds, animals, and bodies of water are very grounding. She told me to walk through the grass with bare feet."

She looked at Robby to be sure he was listening. "She also said to listen to uplifting music when I feel my energy is low. She suggested moving my body by taking a walk or exercising. It may sound cliché, but the fact is that all of these ideas work. So does watching inspiring movies and reading books that make you laugh, smile, or just feel better about life."

"That makes sense. I know music works for me every time," said Robby, "but sometimes it's so hard to do something beneficial when I feel like crap. It's funny how misery tends to want to remain miserable. Like they say, 'Misery loves company.' Instead of being drawn to anything or anyone who will improve my mood, I'm more drawn to other people who are unhappy when I feel this way. Why is that?"

Matt looked at Mary. "You want to take this one?"

Mary walked into the living room from the kitchen. She placed the flowers she'd just arranged on the coffee table in front of Robby. "It's all about energy again," she said. "Our emotions are connected to our thoughts. Better said, our emotions are a result of our thoughts. But we tend to be in greater control of our thoughts than our feelings when we're feeling emotionally flooded. When we're in a bad mood, the energy created by that mood fills our entire body and mind. It not only wants an energetic match—other miserable people—it also draws people and events to us that resonate with the same vibrational frequency. Since your entire body and mind are in that vibrational state, it's going to resist any thought you have about changing it to a higher frequency."

"Precisely," said Matt. "This is why it's important that you know what your miserable mood is going to attract. Like Mary said, you won't just attract other miserable people into your life; you'll attract miserable-frequency events and circumstances, too. Once you know this intellectually, especially if you know it from experience, it's usually enough to get you to turn on some uplifting music to help alter your mood."

"With that understanding, Robby," added Mary, "do you know why you turned on the news in the wake of losing your mala?"

"Yeah, basically to perpetuate the anxiety I was already feeling, right?"

"Boom! You got it, man," said Matt. "I almost forgot. You know, there's a reason you lost your mala in the first place. Do you know why, Grasshopper?"

"So everything I've gained can now fall apart?"

"Wow! You're a terrible student. You just give in to the resistance, don't you?"

"I'm kidding. It's just that my entire life turned around for the better after I found that mala. I'm a little attached. So sue me."

Matt looked at Mary and rolled his eyes. "The reason you lost your mala is because it's time to move on from it," said Matt. "It's time either to get a new one or to focus on your intentions in a new way."

"I guess I'm just not there yet," said Robby.

Matt looked at Mary. "You should escape his wallowing until he's ready. Call Caroline to do something. I think she's got the day free."

She looked at Robby with sympathy. "Thanks, Matt, but I'm going to stay and take care of . . . let's see, how would you say it, Pitypuss?"

They all laughed.

"Suit yourself, Masochistic Mary. Try not to bring the world down with you."

Matt pointed at Robby. "We're leaving in three days. If your mood doesn't improve, I'm driving to New York City by myself."

"He'll be fine," Mary replied.

Matt gave Mary a kiss on the cheek, tousled Robby's hair as he walked by, and headed out the door for work. As he was walking down the stairs toward his car, he heard Robby yell from inside, "Thanks, Matt!"

CHAPTER TWENTY-EIGHT:

THE RECOGNITION

AFTER MARY VISITED her parents' gravestone, she walked around the cemetery in order to give Robby some extra time. She liked walking around cemeteries. There was something peaceful about them to her. She had been visiting this particular one since she was ten, after her mother was buried there. She found it interesting to read the headstones and imagine who the people named on them once were. She especially loved the older headstones from the eighteenth century.

Robby was halfway across the cemetery. He kneeled before his own mother's headstone, staring at the photograph of her that he'd brought with him. *I wish you could see me now, Mom*, he thought. *I've come a long way since you were here. I've given up ghostwriting and hope to make a living writing my own books, just like you encouraged me to do years ago. It took me this long to get up the nerve.*

Robby picked the weeds from around her headstone and collected some leaves that had gathered next to it, throwing them aside. *I've learned so much about how life really works, Mom. I think you'd be proud of me. I'm much happier now. Dad's been a big help. You'd be proud of him, too. He's really turned his life around. He's so healthy it's like he's a different person. He told me you came to see him. And you know I dreamed of you myself. I don't know if any of it is real. If you could send me a sign, make it something that's unquestionable if you can. I'm not the skeptic I once was, but some things are harder for me to believe than others.*

A crow was cawing on a tree branch nearby. Robby looked at it. *If that's you trying to send me a sign, it's not enough. We have so many crows in New England, how can I make that leap? But I still like it. Don't stop. It's a nice coincidence. Still, if you can do something a little more obvious, maybe downright blatant, that would be helpful.*

Robby saw Mary heading toward him and knew he needed to wrap up his visit. *Mary has to go to work now, Mom. I'll see you next week. Wish me luck in New York. I miss you so much. Love you.*

Robby kissed his fingers and placed them on the headstone. He stood up and hugged Mary, then they walked arm in arm to the SUV.

Robby dropped Mary off at work since his pickup truck was getting a tune-up. When she arrived for her shift at Jankowitz Jewelers, Eva was all smiles. "Why are you smiling so much?" Mary asked.

"No reason. Just happy."

Some customers walked through the door and Eva walked over to help them as she told Mary, "Mr. Jankowitz wants to see you downstairs."

Mary snickered at Eva's bizarre behavior and went down into the basement where Mr. Jankowitz worked. As she got to the bottom of the stairway, he was in the middle of doing something to a gold ring with a torch-like apparatus. He had his peculiar-looking goggles on that Mary thought made him look like a mad scientist. He didn't seem to notice she was there. She considered going back upstairs, but he shut down the torch and took off the goggles before she did.

"There you are, Mary. I have some news for you," he said. He swung around on his stool and patted the stool next to him. She sat down and wiggled back and forth on the revolving stool.

"I was at a gemstone show in Boston last weekend and happened to show some other jewelry store owners a few of your drawings. They were all very impressed." Mr. Jankowitz grabbed one her drawings that he had been using to create a ring. Mary anxiously waited to see where he was going with this. "Anyway, Mary, after showing your drawings to people, seven jewelry store owners between here and Boston are now interested in hiring you to come to their store one day every month or so."

Mary's jaw fell open, which was the response Mr. Jankowitz was expecting.

"I told them you charge seventy-five dollars per drawing and that they'd need at least four customers in order for you to make the commute. I also told them you charge thirty-five cents per mile. So you already have eight clients, including me. That's two a week right now, and I'm sure the word will quickly spread."

Mary did the math in her head. *Four customers at seventy-five dollars is three hundred dollars, times two stores a week . . .* "That's six-hundred dollars a week!" she blurted out.

Mr. Jankowitz snorted in amusement. "Yes. Are you interested?"

Instead of answering, she leaned over and gave Mr. Jankowitz a kiss on the cheek. He blushed, and she was quite sure she saw a smile in there somewhere.

"I'll take that as a yes. Just one thing, Mary. I still want you to work here. So I hope you'll consider staying, even though you'll likely need to cut down on your hours. But if you're going to quit, please give me enough notice to find someone new to replace you, okay?"

"I'll work my schedule around the drawings, sir. I love working here. Thank you."

She began to walk away but then stopped and asked, "Mr. Jankowitz? Why are you being so generous? I mean . . . I know you're a generous man, and I'm grateful . . . but why help me with something that might lead me to stop working here someday?"

Mr. Jankowitz looked at Mary over his eyeglasses that were halfway down his nose. "I knew you were special the day you came in here to sell your mother's ring. I'd never met anyone who negotiated as well. It made me realize that I needed someone in the store who had those skills. Later that day after you left, I told Eva, 'If you ever see that young woman again, offer her a job.'"

"I thought you hired me because the last clerk left."

"We needed you because she left. I would have hired you even if she had stayed. That clerk you replaced, all she did around here was paint her nails and stink the place up with the smell of nail polish. Few people have what you have, Mary. I probably shouldn't tell you because you'll ask for a raise, but we've increased our sales by thirty percent since you started."

Thanks to my daddy, she thought silently to herself.

Mr. Jankowitz continued. "I don't want you to leave. But you're the type of person who is ultimately destined to work for herself. Entrepreneurship offers you unlimited opportunity both creatively and financially. I want that for you. So I'm trying to help you do that while you're still here."

He paused for moment, then said, "Honestly, I don't know what Eva and I are going to do around here without your smile to brighten

this place up. We'll just have to deal with that when the time comes."
Mr. Jankowitz appeared to be getting misty-eyed. He turned away, put
his goggles back on, and relit his torch.

Mary skipped away and bounced up the stairs. Eva was watching
the customers while waiting for Mary. They were considering buying
some expensive earrings. She still had the smile on that she'd had when
Mary arrived for work.

When the customers left, Eva put the earrings back into the case
and approached Mary with excitement. "You're going to have to teach
me this intention thing you're doing," she told Mary. "I never thought
Mr. Jankowitz would share you with anyone, especially at the risk of
losing you."

"I must admit that I'm surprised myself," Mary replied. "But that's
the power of intention. I'll show you how if you're interested."

Eva nodded quickly and smiled.

"Great, let's begin now," said Mary. She walked Eva over to the
jewelry case with the mala beads. "Are you drawn to any of the gemstones in particular on the malas we have here?"

Eva pulled out the light blue amazonite mala beads and held them.
"I've had my eye on this mala for a couple weeks. Someone almost
bought it, and I was so glad when she didn't."

Mary closed the case. "I'm buying that one for you, then," she told Eva.

"Oh no, Mary. I can't accept it."

"Please, Eva. I've wanted to find a way to thank you for the kindness you've shown me since the first day I walked into this store. It
would be my pleasure to give you your first mala."

Eva hugged Mary and asked, "So this is what your husband used
to turn his life around the way he did?"

"Yes. And if they can work for Robby, trust me, they'll work for
anyone."

The women broke out in laughter.

For the remainder of their shift, Mary taught Eva everything she had learned about using the mala from Robby and Caroline. Eva began using it that evening when she got home. She was very excited about getting in touch with her inner connection to the divine.

CHAPTER TWENTY-NINE:
THE THREAT

ROBBY WOKE UP to a beautiful, sunny day. He grabbed himself a cofftea and stared out the living room window overlooking the reservoir. The water reflected the sunlight in a way that was almost too bright to look directly at it.

"Sure is nice to wake up to that view, huh?" said Mary, who had come from upstairs and was walking into the kitchen. She grabbed herself a coffee and sat beside Robby.

Robby looked at her with a warm smile. "I'm really glad you got us into this place. It's so much more inspiring than the old place."

"I know, right? I love it, too. Guess what I'm doing in a little while."

"No idea. What?"

"Giving Jenny a painting lesson."

"Our landlord?"

"Yeah. We're going to paint flowers in the garden."

"That's what I'm talking about. You never would have done that at our old place."

"I know. I can't believe we live here." They both took sips of their coffees. "How are you feeling about losing your mala these days? Any different?"

"To be honest, I'm still looking over my shoulder, expecting something bad to happen, like all the good that came from the mala is going to fall apart. Look what happened with my truck. Can you believe it's going to cost fifteen hundred bucks to rebuild the transmission?"

"Robby, you expecting something bad to happen is no different than you setting the intention that bad things are going to happen. Did you learn nothing from practicing your mala and the lecture Matt gave you about the news?"

The phone rang, startling them both. Robby kissed Mary on the top of her head, walked into his office, and answered the phone. "Robby Robinson," he said.

"Mr. Robinson, I'm attorney James Calhoun from Calhoun, Bristol, and Cummings. Do you have a moment to talk?"

"Ahh, sure. What's this about, Mr. Calhoun?" Robby wrote the attorney's name down on a notepad.

"My client is Susan Davenport. I understand you received a down payment from her late husband, Dale, in the amount of fifteen thousand dollars. She feels that she is entitled to a refund considering he has died and you did not finish the book."

Robby's entire body stiffened. *I have to stop picking up the phone when I don't know who's calling,* he thought to himself.

"Look, Mr. Calhoun, I have deep compassion for Sue's loss and I'm saddened by Dale's death, too, however I have a contract that says the down payment is nonrefundable. Dale signed it. There's a reason it's nonrefundable, which is that I turn down offers from other potential clients when I accept a new client. Those potential clients find other ghostwriters. So when something like this happens, when a client dies, it can take months before I find a new client. Plus, Dale and I worked on his book together diligently for weeks. I earned that money already. In fact, I was going to be asking him for the next twenty-percent installment of my fee the very day he died. I'm sorry, but I won't be giving Sue a refund. Quite frankly, I can't believe a multimillionaire is concerned about fifteen thousand dollars anyway."

"It's not the amount, Mr. Robinson. It's the principle. Dale paid you a down payment for something that never got finished."

"Actually, he paid me for services rendered. Because I expected to earn seventy-five thousand from that book, now I'm sixty thousand short. Does anyone care about that?"

"If you don't agree to the refund, then perhaps we'll need to take this to the next step."

"Which is what, exactly?" asked Robby.

"Litigation, I'm afraid."

"She's going to sue me for fifteen grand that I already earned? It will cost her more in lawyers' fees than she'll get if she wins."

"Yes, but it will also cost you more, too. Like I said, it's the principle."

"The principle at hand should be that she follow her husband's wishes because he was the one who signed the contract that said it's a nonrefundable down payment."

"We'll be in touch, Mr. Robinson." James Calhoun hung up without waiting for a response.

"Okay, thanks so much for the call," said Robby, knowing he was talking to dead air. Robby hung up the phone and sat in silence. *First my truck breaks down, and now I might be sued?* he thought. *I keep telling everyone that losing my mala is a bad omen, but does anyone listen?*

He called Matt and arranged to meet him for a beer. He knew Matt was the best person to talk him off the ledge.

CHAPTER THIRTY:

THE HARD LESSON

MATT WALKED INTO Murphy's Restaurant and Bar and spotted Robby sitting at a table in the bar area. There were mirrors sporting the names of liquor brands hanging on all the walls alongside framed photographs of Ireland that looked like they had been taken fifty years prior. Matt sat down across from Robby at a round pub table with tall stools. "You order yet?" he asked.

Robby nodded, looking behind Matt, to signal the beers were on their way. The bartender placed them on the table. "Two Guinness at your service, gentlemen."

"With a shamrock on top. Nice," said Matt, referring to the way the bartender formed a shamrock in the foam on top of the beer.

The bartender left, and Robby said, "Thanks for coming, Matt."

"Of course. I'm always up for a beer."

"I haven't been here since Mary and I saw Stan that night."

Matt chuckled as he sipped his stout. "Let's hope he doesn't pop in while we're here. So what's going on, Numbnuts?"

"A little bad luck since I lost my mala. First my truck broke down. Now Sue Davenport is suing me."

"Suing you? No, wait—you said her lawyer only threatened to sue you."

"Yeah, but the way things have been going . . ."

"You gotta stop. That's something that might never happen, so don't turn that negative possibility into an affirmation that you send out to the Universe."

Robby ignored his last comment. "You can't deny that bad things have happened since losing my mala—the truck breaking down and Sue's lawyer calling happened back to back. So you have to admit that I wasn't being paranoid after all."

Matt looked around the room.

"What are you looking for?" asked Robby.

"To see if anybody else heard the nonsense that just came out of your mouth. You're a riot, you know that? You're like a dog chasing his own tail and wondering why he keeps getting bitten."

Robby laughed. "Wow, that's quite a visual."

"You have to change the angle from which you're seeing this, dude. It's like you're trying to convince me that losing your mala has brought doom to your life. Do you know how warped that perspective is?"

"Illuminate me because I honestly don't see it. From my perspective, everyone around me is living in some kind of denial about what's really happening."

"Robby, it's not that losing your mala beads attracted something bad into your life. It's that your belief that losing your mala beads is going to attract something bad attracted exactly what you expected. Expectation is a powerful force. Your constant looking over your shoulder for a negative consequence is the attention you gave that belief. It's probably why your truck broke down, and I'm sure it's what attracted Sue to hire a lawyer to threaten you with a lawsuit."

Robby ran a hand through his hair and leaned back on his chair. "Go on because I'm still not buying it."

"My point is that the truck and the lawyer had nothing to do with losing your mala, except that losing your mala is what created your fear. Your fear fueled your belief that you are vulnerable without your mala. Fear plus belief plus expectation equals a matched response from the Universe. In this case, your fear, plus your belief that losing your mala is unlucky, plus your expectation of something bad happening, led you to get exactly what you expected—a negative consequence.

"See what a powerful being you are, my fearful friend? You are divinity in physical form. And look what you created all on your own!"

"So you're saying that I created what I feared," said Robby. "Well, I guess it's possible. It seems a bit chicken or the egg, but I must admit that my fear of something bad happening after losing my mala did come before my truck breaking down and Sue's lawyer calling. I guess what you say could be true."

"Oh my god, Knucklehead finally gets it." Matt lifted his drink in the air. The men tapped their mugs together and took a sip.

"What do you think I should do about Sue? Should I hire a lawyer?" asked Robby.

"Can you afford a lawyer?"

"Well, no. I guess not."

"Then use your thoughts to make it go away. Visualize Sue letting you off the hook in some way. Look, if Dale signed the contract, she can't win. So visualize Sue letting it go. You might even want to pray to Dale to help you out. He's in a place of influence now."

"What other choice do I have, right?"

The bartender dropped off two plates of marble cheesecake and two spoons. "Did you order this?" asked Matt.

Robby was already eating his. "Our beers are nearly full. We need something to go with them." Robby then abruptly dropped his spoon and began sniffing the cheesecake.

"What are you doing?" asked Matt.

"Do you taste peanuts or peanut butter in this? It might be in the crust."

Matt took a bite and held it in his mouth to evaluate. "Crap! I think I do."

Robby jumped up and quickly went over to the bartender. "Do you know if there's anything peanut in this cheesecake, maybe in the crust?"

The bartender's eyes widened. "You allergic?"

"Yes, deathly."

"I'll go check the ingredients." He ran downstairs to the kitchen. Two minutes later, he was back with the cheesecake box. "Yes. There are peanuts in the crust."

"I have to rush to the hospital. How much do we owe you?"

"Just go," the bartender ordered. "No charge."

Matt had been through this before with Robby, so he knew what to do. They rushed to Matt's car so he could drive Robby to the hospital. "UMass Memorial Medical Center?" asked Matt as he hustled out of the parking lot.

"Yup." Robby was sipping water from a water bottle Matt had in his car to ease the pain of his swelling lips and throat. He'd been through this several times before. "Stop at the pharmacy first."

As Matt drove, Robby asked, "Who frigging hides peanuts in the crust of cheesecake, especially in this day and age with so many kids allergic? Is it really worth the risk?"

Matt raced into a CVS parking lot and Robby jumped out and ran into the store. He located the antihistamine aisle and found a box of Benadryl. He ripped open the package right in the aisle and swallowed four twenty-five-milligram capsules. He ran over to the pharmacist's cash register. The pharmacist was busy behind the counter.

"I'll be just a minute," he told Robby.

"I'm having a nut allergy and am rushing to the hospital. I'm at risk of anaphylactic shock or cardiovascular collapse. Can I just leave you a ten?" Robby showed him what he was buying.

The pharmacist nodded and Robby threw a ten on the counter, then he ran out of the store. Matt was waiting in his car right outside the door.

"Did you stop to look at magazines or something?" he asked as Robby got back in the car. Matt noticed that Robby's eyes were shutting closed, his lips were swollen, and his breathing was labored. "You look like hell," he told him as he zipped out of the parking lot, down the street, and onto the highway.

"I might be going there any minute."

"You? Mr. Do The Right Thing? I don't think you're going to hell. Can you breathe?"

Robby wheezed. "My lungs feel like they're filling with fluid, and my throat feels like it's closing, even though I know that's not technically what's happening."

"Don't you carry an EpiPen?" asked Matt.

"I did. They expire! And I have a large deductible on my health insurance, so guess what? I couldn't afford to keep buying them."

Robby's eyes were watering, his nose was draining, and he was sneezing like he had a terrible case of hay fever. Robby attempted to look at his cellphone through his eyes that were merely slits by this time. He managed to call Mary in spite of everything. He connected with her voicemail. "Mary, we're on our way to UMass Medical. I ate something with peanuts in it. We just arrived. Love you."

Matt parked at the emergency entrance parking, flew out of his door, and helped his friend walk from the car to the hospital. Robby could barely see, so he needed guidance. Halfway to the door, Robby stopped walking.

"Keep walking, man. What are you doing?" said Matt.

There was no response. Robbie looked faint.

"Robby? Robby?"

They just stood there for twenty seconds, and then Robby seemed to come back into his body. "Holy crap. That was a new symptom I've never had before. I whited out."

Matt walked him through the door. "What do you mean you whited out?"

"Everything just turned white in my head, and my hearing disappeared as if someone had turned down the volume in my ears. That was kind of scary."

Matt led Robby to the triage nurse's station. "How can I help you boys?" she asked.

"I'm having a peanut allergy."

The nurse took his name, and Matt helped him get his insurance card out of his wallet.

"I'll do this later," she said. "Come with me."

Matt stood in the waiting room, but Robby yelled, "Matt, come! I need an advocate." Matt quickly followed.

The nurse walked Robby right into the ER, got him on a gurney, and a doctor and another nurse came over. One nurse took off his shirt and began sticking wires to his chest. The other nurse inserted an IV into his arm and taped it to his skin. The doctor took his pulse, his blood pressure, and listened to his chest.

"Robert, I'm Doctor Langley. Did you take any medication for your allergy?"

There was no response. Matt stepped forward and said, "He keeps whiting out every so often. He told me his vision turns to white and his hearing disappears for half a minute."

The doctor looked at one of the nurses nervously.

Robby's eyes opened, and he looked around like he was confused.

"The doctor wants to know what you took at the pharmacy," Matt told Robby.

Robby pulled the Benadryl box out of his back pocket and handed it to the doctor. "I took four of them."

The doctor read the box and then gave him an injection. "This is epinephrine. It will keep your heart going. You're probably going to feel a little shaky and cold at first, but it's just temporary."

"I know. I've done this before. It also makes me emotional." Robby looked at Matt. "If I get emotional, it's just the drugs talking."

"Either way, I'm still going to tease you about it later, man," said Matt.

Robby's body began to shiver, and his hands trembled. His eyes teared up. One of the nurses put a blanket on him and held his forearm. She spoke quietly. "You're going to be all right, Robby. It'll be over in a few minutes."

The doctor walked over and gave him another injection. "This is a very high dose of antihistamine. Now you're going to get sleepy."

Robby looked at Matt. "You can go now," he said. "I'm about to fall asleep for about four hours. Thank you for everything. I'm sure Mary will arrive to pick me up." Before Matt could respond, Robby's eyes closed and he was asleep. Matt stayed by his side and waited for Mary.

While asleep, Robby dreamed he was with his mother. They were standing in the grass on the side of the highway. In front of them was his mother's car. It was in the ditch and the eighteen-wheeler that had hit her car was on top of it. Robby looked at his mom. "Why are we here?" he asked. "This isn't something I want to see."

"There was no avoiding the accident, Robby," his mother told him. "I saw it coming. People think I didn't, but I did. I swerved and went into the ditch. That's when the truck hit me. There was no way you could have prevented this if you were with me. You can't prevent fate."

He looked at his mother. "I don't understand. Why did it happen, Mom? Were you thinking negatively or something?"

Margaret laughed softly. "No, honey. It was my time to go. No one dies by thinking negatively. You can attract negative circumstances into your life, but not death."

"Then what did you do to deserve to die? Did you do something bad?"

"You don't understand, Robby. Death is not a punishment. Death is our home. It was my time to go home. And there were lessons that you and your dad needed to learn by losing me. It will all make more sense when it's your turn to come home."

Suddenly they were no longer standing on the side of the highway. Now they were standing side by side on a beach. The smell of salt water pervaded the air, and seagulls were flying above them. The ocean waves were rushing onto the shore. Robby looked around, but he was less concerned by his surroundings than he was about getting answers.

"Like what? What could I possibly learn from your death?"

"You've already learned one of your most important lessons, sweetie—that you have the power of creation right inside your own mind."

"You mean with the mala? But I lost it."

"You lost it, yet you kept creating. Look what you did with your truck's transmission. And imagine influencing Sue to hire a lawyer like she did. She's actually a very kind person. It was completely out of character for her. All of that was your doing—your incredible power of creation."

"So it's true, what Matt said? I really did all that? Did I also create the peanut-crusted cheesecake?"

"You didn't bake it," said Margaret with a grin, "but you certainly drew it into your life, yes."

"So you're telling me that it was never the mala that created the positive changes in my life?"

"That's right. It was you who did all that. Pretty neat, huh?"

"So it really wasn't a magic mala. The mala taught me how to utilize my own magic."

"Using your mala, you communicated to God what you wanted, son. Few people do that. You did it twice a day. As simple as that sounds, from my perspective here it's quite rare and amazing. I have witnessed your prayers—your mantras—traveling through the cosmos like shooting stars."

"Where do people's prayers go?"

Margaret scratched her head. "I can't say I know exactly. Let's just say they go where they need to go in order to manifest into reality."

Robby looked at his mother, shaking his head from side to side. "But you didn't need to die in order for me to learn what I did. I'm sure I could have learned it with you here."

"I didn't die purely for your benefit. I died because it was my time to go home. It's a grand plan that's above my pay grade to know, so to speak. A person's death is never about just one or two people. It's a master design that has infinite implications." Margaret kissed Robby on the cheek, and in a flash he felt a sense of peace wash over him.

She continued. "Here's what I know, and I don't know everything, Robby. You would never have struggled financially while I was alive.

Your father and I would have taken care of you by giving you money. Yet when I died, your father lost his affluence, so he was no longer able to help you. It was your financial struggles that led you to open your mind to the mala. Discovering the magic inside of you occurred as a result of my death. And since my life was over whether or not you learned that truth, I'm certainly pleased that you gained this as a result."

Robby took a deep breath and exhaled slowly. "I think I understand, Mom."

"Good, because I have to go. It's time for you to wake up. I love you, honey."

Robby woke up. He opened his eyes and saw Mary and Matt were sitting next to him in the hospital ER.

"Mary. Matt. How long was I out?" he asked in a groggy voice.

"About four and a half hours," said Matt.

Mary leaned over and kissed Robby on the forehead.

"Man, I just had the weirdest dream," he told them.

The doctor overheard him and said, "Yes, that tends to happen when we give patients the high dose of antihistamine I gave you."

Robby was too sleepy to respond. It took him about twenty minutes to fully get over his drowsiness. After forty minutes, the doctor released him. Robby's eyes were still swollen and he was moving very slowly as his wife and friend helped him to Mary's SUV.

As they reached the car, Mary asked, "What the hell, Robby? You know better than to eat something without asking about the ingredients. Especially dessert."

Robby shrugged his shoulders. "I guess it was meant to be. I learned a very valuable lesson from all this."

"What's that?" she asked.

"That I'm a very powerful manifestor. I can attract good things into my life or I can attract bad things. I get what I believe I'll get. I just wish one thing."

"What's that, buddy?" said Matt.

"I wish I wasn't such a slow learner."

Matt and Mary looked at each other as they both shouted, "So do we!"

CHAPTER THIRTY-ONE:
THE ALTERNATIVES

MATT DROVE UP to Robby's condo in his BMW. He got out, grabbed the suitcase sitting on the steps, and tossed it in his trunk. A few seconds later, Robby came out, jumped in the car, and they were off to the Big Apple.

"You feeling better, Boogerbutt?"

"I am. Much better."

"Thank God. If you get one more peanut allergy when I'm with you, you won't need me to rush you to the hospital because I'll kill you myself. That's nerve-racking! Please don't do that again."

"I'm sorry. I'll be more cautious about checking the ingredients at restaurants." Robby paused for a moment, then said, "Hey, you'll never guess who emailed me."

"If I'll never guess, then just tell me. Who?"

"Sue Davenport. She actually apologized for sicking her lawyer on me. She said that some friends of hers got inside her head, but once her attorney told her what I said to him, she understood better why the down payment was fair."

"Had you visualized her doing something like that, like I suggested?"

"I did. I guess it worked."

"So no more grieving for the mala then either?"

"No more grieving. I do miss saying my mantra one hundred and eight times twice a day. I can't very well keep track on my fingers."

"That's okay. If that's all you're worried about, you can always get a new mala."

"You know that dream I had at the hospital?"

"The one you told us about outside the ER?"

"Yeah. I don't know if it was really my mother visiting me or if it was just a dream. It's still difficult for me to believe it was Mom without proof. Regardless, that dream really helped me."

"How is that?" asked Matt.

"It helped me truly recognize that it wasn't the mala that improved my life. It was me. The mala taught me how to work with an intention. It served as a tool to use in order to do it. And it helped me create a ritual for focusing my mind on what I want without the distraction of my critical, negative self-talk interfering." Robby looked at Matt. "Pretty good, huh?"

Matt was temporarily distracted by an eighteen-wheeler pulling into his lane. As he moved into the fast lane and zipped around it, Robby braced himself in his seat. Matt looked over at him to indicate he had been paying attention to what he said.

"Awesome, man. Can I add to that? Cause I've been waiting all summer for you to understand this," said Matt.

"Sure, please. You'll say it better than I did anyway."

"The point of the mala is not to make you believe it is magical," Matt said. "The point of the mala is to teach you that YOU are. You have the power, dude! You've had it all along. With or without a mala, you are the being that's connected to the Universe. That's what I've been trying to tell you. I'm glad your mother was finally able to drive that message home to you."

"Me, too. Even if it was only a dream, it was damn helpful."

Matt laughed. "You know, your story kind of reminds me of *The Wizard of Oz*. Dorothy needed to learn what was important in her life. Her journey to Oz taught her that there's no place like home. You needed to learn that you have the power within you to create your life. The mala taught you how to do that using your thoughts, words, and actions."

"Great," said Robby. "You've reduced my epiphany to a fairy tale."

Ignoring Robby's comment, Matt added, "That's all the Universe wants from us, Robby. We are here to create."

"Create?" Robby asked.

"Yes, create. Parents create a life during lovemaking. Architects, engineers, and construction workers create houses, skyscrapers, and cities. Entrepreneurs create businesses that employ people. Authors create books that parents read to their children. Artists create artwork that beautifies homes and offices. Filmmakers create movies that entertain families. Musicians create music that uplifts and inspires people. We create even when we don't know we're creating. And how do we do that, Robert? You know this one."

"By what we think, what we say, and what we do."

"That's it. So listen, buddy, because I don't want you to be mistaken about this. Repeating your mantra a hundred and eight times is only one way to focus on your intention without allowing your critical self-talk to contradict it. It's not even how many times you say it that matters. It's really about the intensity of your focus."

Robby had never considered that before.

"We live in a dimension of time, so you can think of it in terms of how much time you spend focusing on your desires, even though that's not entirely accurate. More accurately, it's about how much you focus on what you want versus how much you focus on what you don't want. Since we tend to think about our fears and worries unconsciously, we need tools like the mala to think about our desires consciously."

"So what do you do if you don't use a mala?" asked Robby.

"I personally prefer using a variety of methods because I get bored easily. I use the mala some days. Other days I do what Mary does—I read my written intention either silently or out loud several times a day.

"You know, Caroline and I used to have one of those white boards on our wall, and we listed all our intentions on it. We wrote things like: 'House off the road by a river,' 'BMW 7 Series,' 'Second store located in Connecticut,' and 'Vacation in Ireland.' Every time we walked by that board, we either read them out loud or just thought about them in our heads. In a year and a half, every one of those intentions manifested for us."

"Wow, that's so easy, too," said Robby.

"Other days I do what Caroline prefers, which is to challenge herself to mention her intention in conversation with others as many times as possible. You'd be surprised how many opportunities you get to talk about it. Instead of talking about the weather, sports, or what's wrong with the world, she talks about what she's working toward intentionally, such as tickets to a concert she wants to attend, selling out her next workshop, or finding a new mentor who can take her to the next level in her personal growth."

"That's an interesting method. I don't know if I could do that when talking with people."

"Why not? People talk about all sorts of things in conversation. It's more interesting than talking about the weather for the tenth time that day. How hard is it to casually mention that you want to see some

Broadway play that's coming to Boston or that you're writing a book and waiting to get a publishing contract? Easy, right?"

"I guess that wouldn't be too weird."

"And then, finally, there's the method that your father prefers. He uses meditation. He relaxes his body and then, once he's in a peaceful state of mind, he visualizes the end result of what he's intending to create. That's how he got healthy again."

Matt stopped talking as he switched from Route 295 to the Mass Turnpike. He waited until they were through the tollbooth before he continued. "Years ago, your old man told me exactly how he uses meditation and visualization. I never realized it could be used for anything other than health. The first time I used it, man, I would just visualize what I would do with the extra money once my business started making more income. I thought about our dream house, which we later purchased. I thought about the vacations we'd take. We've taken a couple of them already. I thought about buying my father an antique Model A Ford. I never got to do that one because of my father's health, but I believe that that visualization helped the most."

"Even though you never got to do it?" said Robby. "Why did that one help the most?"

"It was something I wanted to do so passionately that I often wept during the visualization." Matt pointed at Robby. "Tell anyone I said that and I'll beat you into the ground."

Robby laughed. "Okay, tough guy. So are you telling me that crying helps your visualization succeed?"

"It's not the crying, specifically; it's the emotion that I felt during the visualization. If you can visualize with your imagination as well as your emotions . . . in other words, if you can add feelings to your visualization, those feelings are like adding fuel to your intentions.

"You have to understand, the reason I cried when I imagined myself giving the Model A Ford to my father was because it was deeply meaningful to me. It was something I'd always wished I could do. I knew how happy it would make my dad, so I easily imagined his joy in my visualization of that scene, and I felt like I was really there. Being there in my mind allowed me to actually feel what I would be feeling in the moment. Consequently, not only was I crying in my imagination, I was actually crying as I visualized the scene."

"That's cool," said Robby. "I think I understand it."

"It was bizarre because even as I did it, I knew that the emotion I was feeling was somehow turbo-boosting my intention of creating financial success in my business. I later discussed this with your dad, and he told me that the emotional component is a well-known metaphysical truth: our feelings make our visualizations more potent."

Robby turned in his seat to face Matt. "When did you talk to my father about all this? Where was I?"

"Are you kidding? When your father had us all over for your birthday that time. When I'd bump into him at the coffee shop. Heck, I'd ask him questions any chance I got. I knew he used to teach this stuff because Caroline was one of his students."

"Oh yeah, he told me that," said Robby. "I always thought he taught philosophy."

"He did. Metaphysics is a philosophical tradition. Caroline was in his college class before we got married. She taught me a lot herself, but I would ask your dad questions whenever I saw him because she always told me what a wise man he is."

Robby leaned his head against the car door window, rubbing his face with his hand. Matt glanced at him and could tell he was upset about something.

"Face it, you were Mr. Journalism back then. You didn't want to hear anybody talk about anything that wasn't backed by science. Even when quantum physicists were proving all these metaphysical concepts, your mind was already closed. That's why nobody talked about this stuff around you. That's the irony, right? Skeptics look at us and think, *What a bunch of naive meat bags.* Until one day, the few who wake up are wondering why no one shared the secrets of life with them."

Matt saw an older car in the breakdown lane and immediately pulled over. He put his flashers on and pulled behind the car.

Robby was taken by surprise. "Whoa! What's going on?"

"Just follow me, Juicyfruit." He and Robby got out and found an elderly gentleman sitting in the driver's seat fiddling with a cellphone. Matt knocked on the man's window, and the man rolled it open.

"Are you a policeman?" the man asked.

"No," said Matt. "We just stopped to see if you needed any assistance."

"What?"

Matt repeated himself, but louder this time.

The man handed Matt his cellphone. "Can you get this to work? I keep it in the car for emergencies. Now that I need it, I can't get it to work."

Matt fiddled with the phone. "The battery is dead, sir." Matt handed it back to him.

"The battery's dead? It was full when I put it in the glovebox."

"When was that, sir?" Matt shouted. He sounded like he was yelling at the man.

"My kids gave it to me for Christmas. They charged it for me, and I put it in here."

Matt chuckled without the man noticing. "You need to charge these things every week, sir."

Robby walked up. "He's got a flat on his right rear tire. Let's just change it for him."

"Sir, did you know you have a flat tire?" asked Matt.

"Of course. That's why I was trying to call Triple A. Do you have a phone I can use?"

Matt looked at the speeding traffic whizzing by and noticed that the man's car was barely in the breakdown lane. "We're happy to change the tire for you. You never know how long you'll have to wait. If you give me the keys, we can get your spare out of the trunk."

He looked at Robby and whispered, "If the spare has any air in it."

The man got out of the car to open the trunk for them and unknowingly stepped into the highway. A trailer truck was heading right toward him. Robby ran up to the man and gently guided him to safety. The man looked at Robby, irritated. "You don't have to push," he told Robby. The trailer truck blew sand on their shoes as it rushed past them. The man didn't notice. "I'm sorry, sir," said Robby. He smirked at Matt.

They waited as the man slowly found the trunk key and unlocked it. The car was old, but it looked like it had never been driven. The trunk was clean and organized. Even the spare tire looked new, and it was a real-sized tire rather than the doughnut style.

"What do you know? It has air in it," said Matt.

A half hour later, the spare was on the car. Robby made sure to place everything back in the trunk the way they found it. The man tried to give them each a five-dollar bill, but they refused. They slowly walked him back to the driver's seat so oncoming cars wouldn't hit him. He thanked them three times for their assistance. The man waved as the young men waved back and watched him drive away.

Once back in Matt's BMW and driving down the Mass Pike, Matt and Robby were each focused on their thoughts for a while. Robby was the first to talk. "Do you always stop when you see a car on the side of the road?" he asked Matt.

"No. When I see something like that, I ask my body if I should pull over to help, and it usually tells me."

"Your body? How does it tell you?"

"Well, I either get a good feeling or a bad feeling, and I've learned to trust it."

"Do you ever feel nothing, like you don't feel good or bad but something in the middle?"

Matt shook his head in amazement of Robby's always wanting a definitive answer. "It doesn't work like that for me. I either feel good or I feel bad. It all happens so fast. By the time I see a car in the breakdown lane, I only have seconds to make a decision. If I take any longer, I'm already past the car, and it would be dangerous to stop and back up. That works in my favor. I go with whatever I feel at that instant."

"Okay. So what if you're in a hurry? Do you stop if you've got a meeting and helping the person will make you late?"

Matt began to realize how much Robby operated from his intellect versus his intuition. "You've been doing this mala bead practice for a few months now, but do you even understand—I mean, *really understand*—what it's all about?"

Robby shrugged his shoulders. He felt it was a trick question.

"Do you believe in spirit guides?" Matt asked him.

"I don't know. I don't *not* believe in them, but I haven't really given it much thought. I did meet a girl at the library who was obsessed with malas, and she said she believes her spirit guides work with God. It was the same day I found my mala."

"Okay, that's a start. And what's her name?"

"Truth."

"Yeah, I want the truth."

"No, that's her name, Truth."

"Seriously? You met a girl at the library named Truth who told you she has spirit guides who work with God?"

"Yeah, why is that so weird?"

Matt just smiled to himself at the amazement of it all. "Have you ever seen this person again?"

"No, just that once."

Matt glanced over at Robby. "Well, this is the point I'm trying to make. Let me just tell you what I believe, and you can take it or leave it."

"Knock yourself out," Robby told him.

"It helps me to understand metaphysics better by believing that we are all guided by some higher power. So I like to imagine that this higher power that I call the Universe gets some help from spiritual beings that I call spirit guides. And I like to imagine that every person has one or two guides that watch over him for his entire life, or her entire life. Are you following me?"

"Yup! Keep going," said Robby.

"Well, I believe that these spirit guides have a higher view of our lives than we do at any given moment. I don't believe they can see too far into the future since we all have free will and can make choices that change our direction at any moment. But I do believe they can see into our more immediate future, perhaps a few minutes or maybe even a few days or weeks ahead, and can see what we'll experience if we don't make any unexpected choices that are out of character for us. Are you still with me?"

"I'm with you."

"So it's these spirit guides who are communicating with us when we talk about the four ways the Universe communicates with us. Remember intuition, coincidence, messengers, and events?"

"I have them memorized," Robby said proudly.

"Great. Using the example of the elderly man with the flat tire, he was driving a 1985 blue Chevy Impala. Well, my mother used to drive a 1985 blue Chevy Impala. I just happened to see a photograph of my mother in front of her car just two days ago, and for some reason it got me thinking about how cool that car was. I've seen that photo a zillion times before, but only two days ago I noticed the car and thought about it.

"So today, two days after I saw that photograph, I see the same car, same year as my mother's, in the breakdown lane. And all I can think of is my mother. In the speed of light, thoughts flash in my mind of how that could have been my mother stranded like that when she still had her car. That's why I noticed the old guy's car, and that's why I quickly felt—notice I said *felt,* not *thought*—that I needed to pull over to help him."

Robby turned to face Matt. "Therefore, it was the coincidence of seeing the photo, thinking about the car, and then seeing that car two days later that made you pay attention. Right?"

"Yes. It was also my intuition because despite the coincidence I still asked myself when I saw it if I should stop. When I did, the feeling I had in my body was an excited feeling, like butterflies in my stomach, rather than a negative feeling like fear or doom."

"I get it," said Robby. "So what you're saying is that your spirit guides set this up for you? Like maybe they intuitively made you notice the photograph a couple days ago so that you would notice the old guy today? Is that possible?"

"Oh, Robby, it's not only possible, I believe it happens all the time."

"What does it mean? Why would your guides do that?"

"Well, Boy Wonder, that's where faith comes in. Sometimes we find out down the road. Sometimes we never know. But we have to trust there's a reason."

"Like what might be a reason?"

"It could be that the old man's spirit guides got my spirit guides to influence me to help him. Or it could be that my guides knew there would be an accident down the road that we have now avoided. Or it could be that we needed to arrive at the hotel at a certain time in order to bump into somebody who is important in one of our lives. The truth is that I don't know and I don't care. I just trust that there's a reason."

"You believe our spirit guides are always trying to direct us in some way?"

"Honestly, it's more that it helps me to imagine it that way. It helps me to think that my guides are my conduit to the Universe."

After a brief pause, Matt added, "To be fair, I don't think our human brains are capable of fully understanding the infinite workings of the Universe and the spiritual dimension. The best we can expect is to have an understanding that's 'true, not accurate,' true to the best of our ability to understand it even though it's not completely accurate from a spiritual-dimension perspective. So my idea of how my spirit guides help me is probably 'true, not accurate,' but that works for me."

Robby looked like he was a bit lost in the conversation. He was back to staring out his passenger-side window.

"The point I'm making is that it's quite a coincidence that you met a girl named Truth who is obsessed by malas on the same day that you found your mala. Don't you agree?"

Robby shrugged his shoulders again. "Now that you say it that way, it does seem like an amazing coincidence."

"A coincidence, right. So what might she have been for you?"

"A messenger?"

"Right. In fact, she might even have been a spirit guide or a guardian angel sent to you from the Universe."

Robby's head lifted like he'd had an epiphany. "She used that phrase . . . *guardian angel.* She said she believed in guardian angels and spirit guides."

"It's almost like she was trying to give you a hint into something," Matt suggested, like he was talking to a child.

"Yeah. You know, she did just suddenly appear out of nowhere. I was reading my mala manual, and the next thing I knew she was just there, staring at me."

Matt added, "I'm not saying she was or she wasn't an angel. I'm just saying that she was a messenger, and it was quite a coincidence that she was obsessed with malas, not to mention that her name was Truth."

Matt tapped Robby on the shoulder. "I don't know what she told you, but I have to believe that she came to you at the right time with whatever message you needed to hear at that moment. And that's what I'm talking about here. We all need to be more aware of these special moments because this is how the Universe helps us along. And that's why I stopped to help the old guy."

"Hmm," was all Robby could say. He was absorbed in thought.

"Oh crap!" said Matt as he lightly hit the brakes.

Robby looked forward. All the cars in front of them were stopping.

"Maybe that was the accident we missed because we helped fix the flat," he said to Matt.

Matt banged his steering wheel. "I don't know. Sometimes a traffic jam is just a traffic jam. All I know is, this sucks."

Matt's BMW rolled to a stop behind the traffic jam. Ten minutes went by before a state police cruiser passed them in the breakdown lane. A few minutes later, an ambulance and a fire truck drove through. After another five minutes, a tow truck followed. Thirty minutes later, traffic began moving slowly. An hour later, they were back to full speed.

As they drove by the accident, Matt noticed that a car had rolled over. He checked to see if it was a Chevy Impala, but it wasn't. There was an SUV that had been sideswiped, which was already hooked up to the tow truck. He looked over to say something to Robby but saw he had fallen asleep in the passenger's seat. They still had four hours of driving to reach Manhattan, so Matt turned on the radio to listen to the sports channel, which was a nice break from being the teacher for a while.

CHAPTER THIRTY-TWO:
THE MISCONCEPTIONS

DAVE ARRIVED AT the hospital to teach his meditation class to patients. Before he got on the elevator, he looked through the window of the chapel doorway to see if Father Burke was around. The chaplain was sitting quietly at the front pew writing. Dave walked up the middle aisle to the pew before Burke sensed he was there.

Dave spoke quietly. "How's my favorite holy man?"

Burke put his notebook and pen down on the bench and stood to greet his friend. "I had planned to come find you when your class was over," he told Dave.

"Well, I have a few minutes before it begins, so I thought I'd see how things went with you and George."

Burke appeared anxious to talk. Dave sat down to indicate his friend had his full attention.

"I'll give you the longer story when we have more time, but I can give you a summary now."

"Do tell, Father. I've been anxious to hear about it."

"Let me begin by thanking you one more time. I had no idea just how much I needed that reunion. We really didn't pussyfoot around and got straight to the heart of what was most pressing on both our minds."

"What else can you say, right? What have you been doing for the last sixty years?" joked Dave.

"It's true. The gist of it is that what I thought was true about my father was simply misinterpretations I had made, just like you suggested might be the case. Your advice was invaluable. I took the time to listen to his side of the story, and I'm so glad I did."

"I'm relieved. Even when we, ourselves, have given this advice to others, we often need someone to remind us of it regarding our own lives. Please go on."

"My father didn't give me up because he didn't love me. He gave me up because he thought it was best for me. Dave, he truly believed he was not equipped to raise me. He has been homeless almost his entire adult life, the only exception being when he was with my mother. And since her death, he's only been sober the last eight years. My mother was his strength, his foundation in every way. When he lost her, he lost a lot more than just his wife. Honestly, their relationship was dreadfully codependent. He was only sober because of her."

"That's very sad," said Dave, waiting for more detail.

"I had no idea he did this, but he watched me grow up from a distance. Any time he could see me playing ball, playing outside the school at recess, or even hanging out with my friends at the Boys Club, he found a way to watch. He kept track of me until I was in my midtwenties. My grandparents helped him follow my progress. He lost track of me when I moved to Boston for a couple years, and then he was never able to figure out where I was after that. Once my parents, who were biologically my grandparents, passed away, he had no one to keep him updated."

"That's pretty dedicated."

"It was, for a homeless, jobless alcoholic. As for him, he was sure that I hated him. Still, knowing his own weaknesses, he felt confident that he had done what was best for me."

"And how are you with all this?"

"I'll tell you the rest at another time. Long story short, it has changed me. It's been nearly a week, and I've been walking on air. A void I've had inside of me for as long as I can remember has disappeared. Frankly, I can't stop smiling. Is that silly?"

Dave felt a sense of relief that the meeting had gone well for his friend, especially since he was responsible for the reunion. "There's nothing silly about it. You found out how much your father has loved you all these years. You made peace with something that has tormented you your entire life. You seem to have eliminated any misinterpretations that troubled you for so long. It would be silly if you didn't feel those things."

Burke hugged Dave. "You're a good friend. How did I get so lucky?"

"Likewise. You want to have lunch today?"

The minister smiled like a boy. "I can't. I'm having lunch with my daddy."

The men laughed.

"I'll catch up with you later," Dave told him.

Dave took the elevator to the third floor and walked to the nurse's station.

"Good morning, Mr. Robinson. Your class is ready," said Betsy. She had a funny smirk on her face.

"What's up, Betsy? What are you up to?"

Betsy led Dave into the conference room set aside for meditation three days a week. Dave walked around the corner and saw that his class had doubled in size. "I didn't know this room could hold twenty people, Betsy," he said.

"It'll hold thirty. After that, we'll need to find another room. You need to stop being so popular."

"It's not me. I'm sure of that. People must be feeling better and spreading the word."

"You're going to put us out of business. Don't you realize that those surgeries and tests are what pay my salary?" Betsy teased. "Never mind, your students are waiting." She patted him on the back and walked away.

Dave welcomed the newcomers, taught about meditation for twenty minutes, and then led the class through a guided meditation for forty minutes. The patients sat in their chairs classroom style, facing Dave in the front of the room, who sat on a comfortable office chair.

When the class was over, one of the patients—a sophisticated woman about sixty years old—approached Dave. "Thank you for today's class, Mr. Robinson," she said.

Dave noticed she was dressed stylishly for a patient. While most of the other people were in pajamas or robes, she was dressed casually in pants and a blouse with what appeared to be a cashmere sweater.

"You're welcome. It's Ruth, correct?"

"That's it. Ruth Horowitz. May I call you Dave?"

"You can call me whatever you want, but Dave works for me. I feel like we've met before. I felt it the first class you attended."

Smiling, she said, "I don't think so. I'd remember a face like yours."

Dave blushed, still trying to recall why she seemed familiar. "I'm sorry. You live long enough and everyone looks familiar, I guess. Did you have a question?"

"Yes. This is my third class. I've come to notice that in every class you slip in little gems of wisdom. I can't seem to categorize it."

"I don't really categorize it myself. But since my background is in philosophy, I'd have to go with *philosophy* or *metaphysics* if forced to give it a name."

"At times it sounds a lot like the law of attraction."

"Geez, I guess some of it might be, but I've never been a big fan of that term."

"No? Why is that?"

"Well, Ruth, I agree with the true law of attraction teachings. I just believe that a few teachings on the subject have missed the big picture."

"What do you think they're missing, Dave?"

"I see two common misconceptions. The first is that they suggest it's all about manifesting material possessions, especially money. At least they neglect teaching that it's about more than those things. I believe money and material possessions are a great way to begin, but the laws of creative manifesting are about consciously using our thoughts, words, and actions to create much more important things in life."

"Like?"

"Like inner peace, health, joy, loving relationships, a sustainable planet, a future for our children. The sky's the limit."

"And the second misconception?"

"The second misconception that I've seen from a few misguided teachings is that they suggest people are responsible for their own illnesses."

"You mean due to their thinking, as if they have attracted it to themselves?"

Dave nodded without speaking. Ruth had touched upon a pet peeve of his, and he was trying to refrain from ranting about it.

"Yes, I've noticed that some teachings would lead one to believe that," she told him.

"Come with me, Ruth." Dave grabbed a wheelchair, had Ruth sit in it, and wheeled her to the elevator. He took her to the fourth floor. They were laughing together when the elevator doors opened. Dave wheeled her up to the nursery window where there were eight newborns being attended to by two nurses.

"I come up here often before class," he said. "I like to look at the babies to raise my vibration."

"Oh my goodness! They're so cute."

"Those two in the corner are not well." Dave pointed them out. "The reason I brought you here is to make my point. These sick babies didn't make themselves sick because they had negative thoughts. Most people don't either."

"That makes sense to me," said Ruth.

"There are a lot of reasons why people get sick, just like there are a lot of reasons people get injured. I don't think anyone should be indicating to the sick or injured that they are responsible for making that happen to themselves."

"So how do illnesses and injuries, including tragedies of all sorts that cripple or kill human beings, fit into metaphysics, Dave?"

"Things will happen to us that we cannot control. Some tragedies and suffering cannot be avoided. You can call it fate. You can call it being in the wrong place at the wrong time. It doesn't matter what we call it. We have to surrender to the fact that bad things might happen to us in our lives. Metaphysics teaches us to accept this truth and understand that there is only one question we can ask ourselves if something bad happens to us. Do you know what that question is, Ruth?"

"I probably don't."

"The only helpful question we can ask ourselves after something bad has occurred is this: given my current circumstances, what can I think, say, and do to move forward in the best possible manner? And this is where the laws of metaphysics empower us. What can I do in this new situation to make the most of my negative circumstances?"

Ruth turned from looking at the babies, cocked her head to reflect, and then looked at Dave. "So you're saying that the laws of metaphysics help us with what we are able to control, which is the present moment, and not with what we cannot control, which is whatever has happened in the past."

Dave's eyes lit up. "You said it a lot better than I did. It's not that I don't believe that we can attract undesirable people, events, and circumstances into our lives with negative thinking—I do. It happens all the time, which is why we must be conscious about our thoughts. I'm just saying that not every bad thing that happens to us is a result of our thoughts, words, or actions. I still believe in fate."

"Fate being what, exactly?"

"Well, that's a big question, isn't it? Let me just say that, to me, I still believe in a higher power that knows what I came into this life to experience. And if getting ill or injured is going to lead me toward that destiny, then who am I to question it?"

"So you don't believe in asking why. Why did this happen? Why me? Why now?" asked Ruth.

"Precisely. Why questions never lead to answers. More importantly, they leave us facing backward, toward the past. People can ask why questions all their lives and never move forward. What? Now that's a better question. What can I do now to get better? What can I do now to improve my life? What is needed in this situation for growth, healing, love, and a more joyful tomorrow?"

Ruth stared at the babies while she listened. She touched Dave's arm and pointed to one little boy she thought was extra cute. They gawked at the babies for a moment before Ruth turned to Dave with a question.

"I understand this is your philosophy, and I'm interested in it. However, how does meditation fit into all this? What got you interested in it yourself?"

Dave grabbed the handles to the wheelchair and wheeled her to the elevator. He talked as they waited for the elevator to arrive.

"You're very perceptive, Ruth. To me, meditation is how I focus on the *what* questions. It's how I get out of my busy thoughts—my worries and fears—and how I focus on my desires. It could be working with a mala, which is another form of meditation to me. It might be praying, also meditation. Or it could be any of the many ways we can focus on our intentions, our desires. These are all various ways in which we meditate.

"People think meditation has to be sitting in front of an altar with legs crossed and palms up on our knees, but I prefer to think of meditation as a method of focus regardless of how my body is positioned. In that way, I can meditate on the subway, in line at the coffee shop, in my doctor's waiting room, and in one of my favorite places, the bathroom."

Dave laughed at his own joke. The elevator doors opened. Dave rolled the wheelchair inside, and then pushed the button for the third floor.

"But what motivated you, personally, to begin meditating?" asked Ruth.

"Well, it wasn't for health reasons, at least not directly. It was more for my mental health. I used to be a bit of a control freak. I believed that in order to be safe I needed to control every little thing in my life, especially my work. I started an advertising agency in my early forties that quickly became successful. Before I knew it, I was working fourteen-hour days and micromanaging everything. It affected my marriage, my relationship with my son, even my friendships, and my business partner was ready to clobber me. For the first time in my life I had money, but the rest of my life was in shambles. And emotionally I was a wreck."

Ruth chimed in. "Then you found meditation?"

"Through divine coincidence I found it. I went to a psychologist, hoping counseling would settle my nerves, and in the first session the counselor suggested walking me through a guided meditation. He used a technique that I still use today, which is the same method I teach here at the hospital, in which you visualize relaxing every part of your body from your head to your feet.

"When that psychologist told me to open my eyes at the end, I couldn't believe how calm I felt. I was so relaxed and peaceful that even he was surprised. He told me that he had never tried it before with any other patient. He was like, 'Wow, this really works!' I left his office and sat in my car for half an hour wishing the feeling would never go away. I knew that once I drove into the city traffic it would disappear, and it did. That's when I began doing it on my own."

"And you've been doing it ever since?" asked Ruth.

"That's right, except for those six years after my wife died, that I talked about in the meditation class. However, the story doesn't end there. It calmed my mind so much that it just naturally led me to stop being such a control freak. That's when I arranged with my partner that he run the company while I taught at the college. Suddenly I had two incomes yet I was working less than half the hours. The advertising agency continued to thrive without me micromanaging it, and I got to share my passion with eager young minds."

"Philosophy and metaphysics?"

"That's it. I taught for over a decade, then quit after Margie passed."

The elevator door opened, and Dave wheeled Ruth onto the third-floor hallway. She got out of the wheelchair. "I can take it from here," she said as she stood up. "Listen, I find all of this fascinating. I'd really like to learn more."

"You have a knack for knowing the right questions to ask, Ruth. I'm curious—are you a teacher yourself?"

"In a sense, I am. I've been an executive at a company in New York City for forty years. I help people communicate their ideas better."

"No kidding. My son is on his way to New York City right now. He's a writer and is going to see a publisher about his manuscript on this very subject."

"Did he learn all he knows from you?"

"Some of it, but he's blessed to have a lot of wise teachers around him."

"I'd love to read it once it's published. You don't happen to have any books on this subject I can borrow now, do you? I'm stuck in this hospital for another few days, and you've piqued my interest."

"I normally don't keep anything with me. Let me see what I have." Dave walked into the nearby meditation room and Ruth followed. He picked up his messenger bag from the corner of the room and opened it. "What are you doing in Worcester if you live in New York City, if you don't mind me asking?"

"My younger sister lives nearby in Holden with her husband and kids. I come as often as I can to see them. I had a minor stroke while visiting. I'm okay. My doctor just kept me to run some tests before I make the drive back home."

"That's scary. I'm glad you're okay." Dave rifled through his messenger bag. "Oh, here you go . . ." He pulled out a stack of papers from his bag. "My son gave me a copy of his manuscript to check his metaphysical teachings for accuracy. It's not finished, mind you. He hasn't written an ending yet. But I don't think he'd object to me lending it to you. Personally, I think it's terrific. Of course, I might be little biased. I'd love to hear what you think about it."

Ruth took the manuscript and tucked it under her arm. She touched Dave's arm again. "I'm very grateful. I'll take good care of it, promise." Ruth walked away.

"So I'll see you in class tomorrow?" Dave asked.

Ruth was already into the hallway when she yelled, "See you tomorrow!"

Nurse Paula walked into the room and whispered to Dave, "She's single, you know."

He looked up at her with a smirk. "Hmm, really?"

Paula left the room as Dave gathered his belongings before heading home.

CHAPTER THIRTY-THREE:

THE SHOT TAKEN

ROBBY WOKE UP in his New York City hotel room. He climbed out of bed and opened the curtains. *Brrr, it's freezing in here,* he thought. He turned off the air conditioner, turned on the heater, and found a lush bathrobe in the closet. He looked out at the city and took a deep breath. "It's going to be a great day," he affirmed aloud.

The sun was already shining brightly. His instinct was to work with his mala, which reminded him that he'd lost it. He immediately felt a sense of doom come over him. To counter this, he began thinking about what his mother had taught him in his dream at the hospital. *It was never the mala. It was always me. I've always had the power of creating. The mala was the teacher and the tool. I am the beacon that communicates to the Universe, and the receiver that pays attention to its guidance. It is I who is at one with everything, including God. The mala is merely how I discovered it.*

Robby felt relaxed and empowered by his new realization. He sat in a chair in front of the wall-sized window where the sun shone in on him. He sat quietly, focusing on each breath, just as his father taught him. With every inhalation, he imagined filling his lungs and body with the light of divine love. With every exhalation, he imagined releasing toxins and negativity. He continued doing this until his body felt relaxed and light. Then he visualized what he wanted to create.

Robby saw himself sitting on the steps of the building where the offices of the publishing company were located. He imagined himself feeling happy and excited while talking to Mary on the phone about his new book contract. He visualized telling her that his advance was enough money to write his next book and that they absolutely loved his manuscript.

Robby felt so much emotion in his heart as he lived through the experience of his joyful visualization that he felt complete relief from his anxiety. He sat on the chair in his hotel room for several minutes as tears rolled down his cheeks. Then there was a knock at the door.

"Room service!"

He'd forgotten he had ordered breakfast before going to bed. Robby wiped his tears, answered the door, and retrieved his food. He was surprised to learn how long he'd been sitting in his visualization. He quickly ate, took a shower, got dressed, and packed his suitcase in order to meet Matt outside the hotel at nine o'clock.

Matt was in his typical chipper mood when Robby threw his suitcase in the trunk and jumped into the passenger's seat.

"Good morning, Babyface!" said Matt.

Robby thought to himself, *Babyface? Not Butthole or Fartbreath?*

"Good morning, Matt. You're being especially kind this morning. What's up?"

"Ah, it's a big day for you. I want to be gentle. Are you prepared?"

"I am. You know, I used visualization this morning. It was really powerful. Time disappeared on me, and I felt incredible when I was done. Heck, I still feel incredible."

"Yeah, it's smart to always set an alarm when doing something like that. I've been late more than once because of getting lost in meditation."

"How about you? Are you looking forward to the convention?" Robby asked Matt.

"You bet. I have a list of things I'm looking to find for my clients. If I can find them, I'll make a profit within a week—a good profit, too."

"If I know you, Matt, you'll find what you're looking for."

Matt smiled. "Look at you, all happy this morning. Well, good thing, 'cause here's your address."

Robby's heart jumped into his throat. The men wished one another luck and Robby hopped out. Matt started to drive away and then quickly stopped. He opened the passenger-side window. Robby walked up to the window.

"Dude," said Matt, "who was it that said, 'You miss one hundred percent of the shots you don't take?'"

"Wayne Gretzky, why?"

Matt threw Robby the hockey puck Gretzky had signed for him as a boy. Robby held it in his hands, shocked and confused.

"Oh please—did you really think I'd sell it on you, man? You can pay me back when you get the big advance. The photo is back at the store. Oh, and remember that quote!"

Robby stood there with his mouth open, holding the puck as Matt zipped away. He looked at Gretzky's signature and thought about all that had taken place since he sold the puck to Matt. He put the puck in his pocket and walked toward the massive granite stairway at the front of the building.

He climbed the front steps and entered a large ornate lobby through a revolving door. Inside, the sounds of people walking and talking echoed off granite-tiled walls and floor-to-ceiling windows. All the trim was made of carved wood painted shiny gold. The lobby ceiling must have been twenty-five feet high.

Straight ahead was an information counter and security desk. Robby walked up to the sharply dressed man behind it whose size alone commanded respect. "I have an appointment at Irving and Kittredge Publishing," he said. "Do you know what floor it's on?"

"Sure," the man said in a deep voice that matched his body size. "The eighteenth floor. You can't miss it once the doors open."

Robby's breathing got deeper with every floor the elevator reached. When the doors opened to the eighteenth floor, he felt woozy. There was an antique mahogany desk straight ahead. "Irving & Kittredge Publishing" was affixed in large pewter letters on the wall behind it. A brunette in her twenties sat at the desk answering phones and switching callers to the appropriate lines. "Can I help you?" she asked Robby with a smile that could have been in a toothpaste commercial.

"I'm here to meet Sean Simon at ten thirty. My name is Robby Robinson." He realized how both names had a double letter—SS and RR. Little things like that always amused him. He looked at his watch to see it was quarter past ten.

"Would you like some coffee or tea?" the receptionist asked.

Robby was about to say no when a young man walked around the corner. "Robby?"

Robby looked over to see a man who appeared to be in his late twenties dressed in blue jeans, a white shirt, no tie, and white Converse sneakers. Robby wondered if he had overdressed. "Yes?" he answered.

"I'm Sean Simon. Pleased to meet you." The two men shook hands, and Sean led Robby down a long hall with offices on either side. Every office was furnished differently, many cluttered with books and manuscripts, unlike what Robby had expected. The entire office smelled like a library. Sean walked into a conference room with an oval table that had about ten leather chairs around it. More manuscripts were piled on the windowsills. Sean sat in the chair at the end of the table and motioned for Robby to sit around the corner to his left. Seconds later, a woman in her forties wearing a peach-colored pantsuit and matching heels walked in. Robby stood up out of respect until she sat down across the table from him on the opposite side of Sean.

"This is Lori Cromwell," Sean told him. "She's one of our top editors." The two shook hands over the table.

"I'm going to let Lori begin. We've both read your book proposal, but she read the entire unfinished manuscript you sent."

Robby took a deep breath, trying not to reveal his nerves. The relaxed feeling he'd experienced after his meditation was now gone.

"Did anyone offer you a drink—water, coffee, tea?" Lori asked.

"Yes, the receptionist. But I'm fine without a beverage, thank you."

"All right then, let me begin by saying that the book you wrote for Samuel is wonderful. We only wish most of the books we publish here were in half as good shape when we get them."

"Thank you. That's kind of you."

"And I've read the two you wrote for other authors that hit the *New York Times* Bestseller List. Did your clients contribute to the writing of those books?"

"No. I interviewed them about their ideas, but I did all the writing."

"Well, then, your writing speaks for itself."

Robby nodded, waiting patiently for her to move on to his manuscript. She pulled the manuscript out from a pile of papers she had placed on the conference table and positioned it in front of her.

"Are you nervous?" she asked him.

"Sure, who wouldn't be, right?"

"You shouldn't be. This book could easily become a bestseller. I love the story, the characters were well developed, and the dialogue definitely kept me engaged. I was drawn into the story as much as the teachings. If we publish it, we'll have to find another title, but that's usually par for the course. Your title, *The Eviction,* is too negative."

Robby swallowed. He wasn't surprised about them wanting a title change. "It was just a working title. Picking a great title is always the hardest part for me. I'm just happy to hear that you like the manuscript itself."

"I did. And I wasn't the only one. I loved it so much that I asked our editor-in-chief and someone in our marketing department to read it, and they both agreed with me."

Sean piped in. "The editor-in-chief almost never reads a manuscript unless we're sure we want it."

Everyone paused. Robby was frozen in anticipation. Lori pulled out another paper from her stack and slid it across the table to Robby. "So I have great news for you. We would love to publish your book, and this is what we're prepared to give you for an advance. Granted, we would give you half up front and the other half once the final edits are made. But I'm sure you understand how all that works."

Robby was already celebrating in his head. He'd heard about stories like this, of first-time authors who got hundreds of thousands for an advance. He took a deep breath and looked at the sheet of paper Lori had slid in front of him.

The first—the only—number he saw on the paper was fifteen thousand dollars. He was sure he was missing something. He looked at it again. Nope. That was their offer. *They built me up, told me my writing is wonderful, that I have a possible bestseller, that the editor-in-chief loved it, but their offer is a fraction of what I get for ghostwriting books,* he thought to himself.

"You're offering me fifteen thousand?" he asked, hoping he was mistaken.

"You don't seem pleased," Lori responded. "The fact that we're offering to publish your book at all is something to be excited about. This is your debut book. We feel that fifteen thousand is a generous offer."

Robby felt deflated and confused. "You gave Samuel more than six times this amount and he's never had a book published either." He regretted saying this the moment the words left his mouth. He didn't even really know exactly how much Samuel got, and he never should have tried to use him for leverage.

"Samuel has a platform, Robby," Lori calmly explained. "Do you know what a marketing platform is?"

"Yes, basically an existing audience who will want to read my book. But does a platform really matter with fiction?"

"To us it does," she said gently. "Your book is fiction, but it will be marketed more like a nonfiction book. It's more of a personal improvement book than it is a novel. For example, we've already sold nearly five thousand copies of Samuel's book on preorder just because he announced his soon-to-be released book to his email list and social media followers."

Lori leaned her head down into Robby's view because he was staring at the conference table. "Do you have a large, fan-based email list?" she asked softly.

"No," he answered.

"Do you have tens of thousands of fans following you on social media?"

"No."

"Do you speak publicly, are you on television or radio, or do you have a popular podcast?"

"No."

Robby had intended on negotiating in an effort to maybe get a higher offer, but Lori's questions made him realize he had no leverage whatsoever. He wanted to walk out and tell them where they could put their offer, but he also realized that it might be the best offer he could get. After all, everything she said about him not having a platform was accurate. He realized he should have gotten a literary agent before approaching a publisher. He humbled himself in spite of his grave disappointment.

"I'm glad you like my book. I was hoping for more, obviously. Still, I'm grateful for your offer. It's actually quite generous considering it's my first book."

"If this book sells as well as we expect it will, you'll have no problem increasing the advance on your next book," Lori added. "And don't forget, we're only talking about the advance here. If the book sells well and earns more than the advance, you will earn more whether we pay it up front or later."

"Except that I'll need to continue ghostwriting to pay the bills, which doesn't allow me time to write another book of my own. That's the big issue for me."

Lori looked at Sean and then back at Robby. "How much would you need for an advance to pay your bills?"

"Well, I typically get seventy-five thousand dollars for each ghostwriting job."

"Plus a percentage of the earnings?" she asked.

"No, I just charge a flat fee."

"Robby, you could have been charging a fee plus fifteen percent of the earnings, at least. Those two bestsellers would have earned you a bundle."

Robby had weighed the pros and cons of charging a percentage in addition to his fee years earlier but had decided the flat fee was less complicated for him. He had never expected that two of his projects would become bestsellers.

"Well, I know that now. I might have made a poor business choice in the past, but that's not what's in question right now, is it? Right now we're talking about my writing, and that, as you have pointed out, is where my talent lies. Do you think you can you do better on your offer?"

"We've already had a big meeting on the subject," said Lori. "I'm afraid the offer stands as it is. We were expecting you to be happy about it. I'm disappointed that you aren't."

Robby sat up straight and consciously raised his energy a little. "I'd like to talk with my wife about this."

Lori grabbed a manila envelope from her stack of papers and handed it to him. "Of course. Here's the contract we're offering. Take it home. Think it over with your wife. Then let us know. If you decide to sign it before the end of the month, we might be able to release it next summer or fall. I only found a handful of edits. I'm sure whatever you write for a final chapter will be just as well written."

Lori stood up, and Sean followed her lead. She shook Robby's hand while saying goodbye and exited the conference room. Sean waited for Robby to gather his things and walked him to the elevators. Robby thanked him one more time before Sean looked at his watch and scurried off.

Robby was happy to get outside the building. The sun was now high in the sky, and the long granite stairway stretching from where he stood to the sidewalk below looked majestic. He saw a spot on the stairway off to one side, away from foot traffic, that looked inviting. He could see a haze coming off the granite due to the sun's heat. He was feeling cold throughout his whole body, so he walked over to that area and sat on the steps. The warmth from the granite instantly soothed him. Robby looked up at the sun to expose his face to its heat.

He felt like such a fool. He was pretty sure he had embarrassed himself back in the conference room. *I really set myself up for disappointment,* he thought to himself. *All that intention work . . . all those days I chanted my mantra with my mala thinking about this moment . . . even the visualization I did this morning, crying to myself in my imagined outcome . . . it sure didn't look anything like this. At least I now have my book's ending.*

Robby's attention was drawn toward a person who had come out of the building and was walking down the stairs. She was about fifteen feet away when he caught a glimpse of her from the side. She was a petite blond woman, a little younger than he, and she was very light on her feet. She seemed to skip from step to step.

Oh my god, that looks like Tru, he thought to himself. *No way! It can't be.* She was now past him and already three-quarters of the way down the stairs toward the street. He stood up to get a better look, but all he could see was the back of her. Still, the way she moved, her lightness of being, was just like Tru. When she reached the street, a taxicab pulled up to her. Robby yelled as loud as he could, "Tru! Truth! Truth!" She turned to look toward the yelling, as did several other people. Then she got into the cab. *That's her! I think. It sure looked like her.* The cab's door closed, and the taxi drove away. *Oh no, no, no. Now I'll never know.*

Robby watched the taxi drive down the street and around the corner. He took a deep breath and sat back down on the stairway. His chest was pounding. *Could that really have been Tru?* he wondered. *What kind of crazy coincidence would bring her here to this city, on this stairway, at this moment?*

He ran his hands through his hair and thought about his conversation with Tru at the library. He recognized he was feeling sorry for himself. He remembered Tru telling him, "What we focus upon expands. If you think happy thoughts, you attract happy people and circumstances into your life. If you think unhappy thoughts, you attract unhappy people and circumstances into your life." Robby made a conscious effort to focus on the present moment and all that was good.

He could feel the warmth of the sun as he sat on the magnificent granite stairway. He held the manila envelope from Lori Cromwell in front of him while leaning his arms on his knees. He thought, *Thank you for the blessings. This book contract is a wonderful stepping stone toward the future writing career I desire. The advance, however modest, is a gift of abundance. After all, I've almost written the book in its entirety. More importantly, Mary and I are happy, healthy, able to pay our bills, and living in a beautiful home. And we are now both on the path to having careers where we can use our talents creatively, even if I have to ghostwrite one more book. We are truly blessed, and I am grateful.*

Robby felt his cellphone buzz, signaling he had a voicemail. He remembered he had shut the ringer off prior to his meeting. He looked at his phone expecting to see a message from Mary, but it was his father who had called. He listened to the voicemail.

"Robby, it's Dad. Call me back. It's important."

Robby dialed Dave's cell number.

"Hey, Robby. Thanks for calling me back."

"Sure, Dad. You said it's important. Is everything all right?"

"Oh sure. I wanted to talk to you before I left the hospital. I just had my meditation class, and I have a patient here who would like to talk to you."

"Oh, Dad, now's not a good time, I have . . ."

Dave didn't listen. "Here she is, son. Her name is Ruth."

Robby sighed.

"Hi, Robby. My name is Ruth Horowitz. Thanks for taking my call."

"Sure, Ms. Horowitz. Nice to meet you." Robby still called anyone over fifty Mr. or Ms.

"Listen, Robby, I have a confession to make. I'm getting some tests done here at the hospital, which is how I met your father. I'm in his meditation class. He and I got to chatting yesterday, and I talked him into letting me read your manuscript. I read it from cover to cover last night. Can't sleep around here, so I was happy to have something to read."

Robby couldn't believe what he was hearing. *My father lent my unpublished manuscript to someone? Are you kidding me now, Dad?* He planned to scold his father the second he got this lady off the phone.

Ruth continued. "To tell you the truth, Robby, I couldn't put it down. All this metaphysical insight is new to me, so I was like a sponge in water. You're a wonderful teacher. More importantly, I like your writing style."

"Thank you, Ms. Horowitz. I appreciate that."

"I really fell in love with the story and its characters. I know that it's fictional, but I assume it's based on real events from your life?"

"Yes. Yes it is."

"And you're a good writer, which is why I wanted to talk with you. Your father tells me you're meeting with a publisher today."

Great. Dad told her my whole life story, he thought. "That's true," Robby said. He wasn't ready to talk about the meeting, so he didn't say anything further.

"Well, Robby, I happen to be an executive editor with a major publishing company myself, Carnegie and Hayward Press. Do you know it?"

"Oh yes. I certainly do."

"Well, I have enough clout at this point to buy a book now and then without needing anyone else's approval, and I'm prepared to make you an offer right now before you sign a contract with another company."

Robby didn't let himself get too excited. He hoped maybe she would offer a little more than fifteen thousand dollars, but he was too exhausted emotionally at this point to care much either way.

"I'm prepared to offer you a two-book contract for one hundred thousand dollars."

Robby was stunned. He wasn't sure he heard her correctly, so he asked Ruth to repeat herself. "I'm sorry. Could you say that again?"

"I said I'm prepared to offer you a two-book contract for one hundred thousand dollars."

She really did say that, he thought to himself. He began to feel excited, but he wasn't sure how to respond to her. Mary's voice rang in his head to negotiate. "Ms. Horowitz, I'm very grateful for your generous offer. How about one hundred thousand for this book with the right of first refusal on my second book?"

Ruth paused. "To be honest, Robby, I don't have the authority to offer more than seventy-five thousand for any one book. So I'll either offer you seventy-five thousand for this book alone or one hundred for this one and your next one. It's your choice."

Robby was glad he was sitting down. He felt unsteady.

"I have a good feeling about this book, Ms. Horowitz. Won't I get a lot more on my second book if this first book does well?"

"If it does as well as I expect it can, you'll get a lot more."

"Okay then, I accept your offer for the one-book contract."

"I like your confidence, Robby. I would have done the same. Can you get to the Avenue of the Americas today? I can have a contract waiting for you, which is very unusual—you probably know. I just really want to publish your book."

"Well, I set the intention that my publisher would love the book as much as I do. So, yes! I can head there now."

"I have your cell number here. I'll text you the exact address. Give me an hour or so. Go have lunch somewhere. Ask for my assistant, Courtney Johnson. She'll have everything ready for you. Let's say, after one o'clock?"

"Thanks, Ms. Horowitz. After one is fine."

"One last thing, Robby. About the title . . ."

"Yes," he responded, "I have a better one."

"What is it?" she asked.

"*The Magic Mala.*"

"Oh that's perfect. Okay, Robby. We'll be in touch soon."

"Thank you, Ms. Horowitz. Goodbye."

Robby hung up, his entire body quivering. He was so happy he wanted to scream out loud. He immediately called Mary who was anxiously awaiting his call. He told her the story of the morning's events and gave her the good news as he sat on the stairway. They cried together in joy and celebrated the moment by phone. When he eventually hung up, Robby sat on the steps a little longer to take in the moment.

Between possibly seeing Tru, Ruth's call, the sun's rays, and the haze from the heat on the granite steps, everything felt oddly surreal to him. All the sounds of the city fell far off into the distance, and Robby looked into the sky wondering if his mother was able to witness his accomplishment from wherever she was now.

As he looked into the clouds, he saw something in the sky above him. It was a tiny dark spot, but it seemed to be moving toward him. It appeared to be almost weightless, like it was floating. But it was unquestionably floating in his direction.

A woman and a man walking up the stairs saw Robby looking up, so they looked up, too. They weren't sure what he was looking at, so they moved closer to him.

"I see it!" said the man. "What do you think it is?"

"Yeah, what is that?" the woman followed.

Robby didn't answer. He just stared at the object above him. Other people walking on the stairs began to notice the three looking into the sky, and they looked up, too. Seven people were now watching this object falling.

Robby cupped his hands, thinking he might try to catch whatever it was, but no effort was necessary. The breeze carried it directly to him until it gently landed inside his cupped palms. When he saw it, Robby became weak.

"What is it?" asked the man.

"Yeah, what is it?" the woman repeated.

Robby held it in his palms as he stared at it in awe.

"It's a crow's feather," he said.

He whispered to himself, " . . . about three inches long . . . with a streak of white at the top."

ABOUT THE
AUTHOR

BOB OLSON, author of the nonfiction title, *Answers about the After-life*, has forayed into fiction for this newest book, *The Magic Mala*. He is a storyteller who aims to inspire readers to improve themselves, follow their passions, and make the world a better place.

When Bob's not writing, teaching, or creating a new podcast episode, you'll find him with Melissa, his wife of more than thirty years, kayaking, bicycling, sightseeing on their Vespa, or eating dinner on their porch with friends and family members. They live in southern Maine with their beloved dog, Libby.

To further your understanding of the ideas presented in this book, the author teaches an online course on the book's website. You can also learn about Bob's podcast and purchase your own magic mala by visiting:

www.TheMagicMala.com

SHARE THE
MAGIC

IF YOU ENJOYED this story, or if the teachings inspired you, recommending this book to friends—or buying them a copy as a gift—is a generous and loving way to share the magic. Everyone remembers the person who recommended to her, or gifted him, the book that changed his or her life for the better.

KEEP THE

MAGIC GOING

THE MAGIC MALA is the perfect book to discuss in book clubs or groups because it helps readers integrate the teachings during their discussions. And while you are focused on the magical possibilities of life, the Universe responds to your focus with more magic.

It's also fun to recognize and talk about your own stories related to the book, such as incidents of messengers, coincidence, divine events, intentions, or the results of your own thoughts, words and actions. If you don't belong to a book club, create your own by asking your friends to meet once a week. It's not only a lot of fun; it's a great way to keep the magic of this story going.

COURSES

THE AUTHOR offers an online course that helps you to understand and apply the life-changing teachings in *The Magic Mala!*

This course, taught by the author, further demonstrates…

- The power of your thoughts, words, and actions
- Setting intentions to transform your life
- Creating powerful mantras that really work
- Why understanding attention vs. intention is necessary
- Alternative tools to the mala you might prefer
- Recognizing guiding signals from the Universe
- How to identify beliefs that are holding you back
- The one belief that blocks most people's attempts to change
- How to stop feeling like a victim
- Simple ways to filter the negativity that makes you miserable
- How to get and expect magic in your life
- The 40-day commitment to begin changing your life today
- Much, much more

To learn more about this course, visit . . .

WWW.THEMAGICMALA.COM

* Download a FREE PDF of
"The Top 5 Mantras to Use with Your Mala"
(on website)

Made in the USA
San Bernardino, CA
09 June 2017